THE TRUE CRIME PUZZLE BOOK

FIENDISH ACTIVITIES,
FROM CROSSWORDS TO QUIZZES

JAMIE KING

summersdale

THE TRUE CRIME PUZZLE BOOK

Text by Emma Marriott

An Hachette UK Company
www.hachette.co.uk

Summersdale Publishers
Part of Octopus Publishing Group Limited
Carmelite House
50 Victoria Embankment
LONDON
EC4Y 0DZ
UK

www.summersdale.com

Printed and bound in China

ISBN: 978-1-83799-368-0

INTRODUCTION

If you're fascinated by true crime – whether in the form of a daring heist, a brutal murder or a cunning cyber scam – or if you simply like a good mystery, then you've come to the right place.

The True Crime Puzzle Book features a devious array of crosswords, anagrams, sudokus, wordsearches, conundrums and more, all relating to famous or lesser-known incidents from history right up to the present day. From high-profile kidnapping cases to organized gangland robberies, the puzzles are designed to test and expand your knowledge.

So, if you think you know your Jack the Ripper from the Zodiac Killer, or if you want to learn more about the greatest diamond thieves in history or Japan's most famous prison escapee, then see if you can crack these puzzles. Welcome to the shocking, sinister and intriguing world of true crime.

ANTWERP DIAMOND HEIST

In 2003, a gang of thieves broke into a vault in Antwerp, Belgium and made off with at least $100 million worth of diamonds, gold and jewellery. Protected by multiple security mechanisms, the vault was supposedly impenetrable, and even today the police are unsure how the gang succeeded. Solve the clues to reveal key elements of the heist.

Across

4. Hair product used to impair thermal motion sensors (9)
6. Wear to avoid leaving fingerprints (7, 6)

Down

1. Copies (of vault keys) (10)
2. Waiting vehicle (7, 3)
3. Planning (11)
5. Incapacitate (alarms) (7)

DETECTIVE BOARDS

When investigating a crime, detectives sometimes compile an evidence or bulletin board made up of photos, maps and various items. This provides a visual record of what they know and helps to highlight connections between people, places and events.

Can you spot the five differences between the two images below?

MURDER SCENES

In the past, investigators at crime scenes marked the location of bodies with chalk lines. Today they use a variety of more modern methods, including taking photographs and videos, using numbered markers or 3D laser scanning.

Match up the chalk outlines. The first one has been done for you.

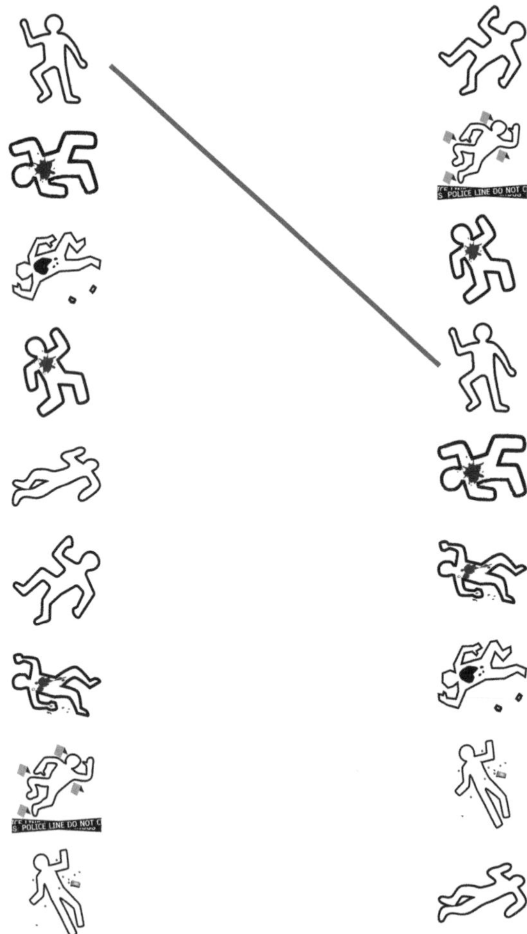

TRIVIA

The 1980 slasher movie *Friday the 13th* features a group of teenagers at a summer camp who fall prey to a serial killer. The movie shares similar details to a real massacre that took place in the 1960s in which three teenagers were mysteriously stabbed to death while camping. Where did this happen?

A. Finland

B. United States

C. Thailand

SUPREMO SWINDLER

Natwarlal was one of the most notorious con artists in India. It's claimed that he even duped a tourist into buying the Taj Mahal. He was repeatedly arrested but escaped from prison nine times, including in 1996 when he was 84 and used a wheelchair. Can you "catch" all the related words below in the wordsearch?

B H R W T R P A S I F M H P E
H B M D H D A M H A M S N G S
I Y W L O E U N K M W K B C U
A K W C K G E E X Y N F X Y O
L G E J G F C L C Q L C X I H
W F I L R H D P C R I Q R E T
F D E C E I I Y R H R X Z L N
V R U Q D J S S L G A O D L E
K V U L F E G M Q S S I M D M
J E L J O R U J B J D Q R A A
S V A E R Y I Y R E G R O F I
T J T B T Q S X H T G Q A G L
P R I S O N E S C A P E S F R
F J Y Y F N S N S L H Y V L A
L A H A M J A T S M E U B D P

DISGUISES	PARLIAMENT HOUSE	SMUGGLER
FAKE CHEQUES	PRISON ESCAPES	TAJ MAHAL
FORGERY	RED FORT	WHEELCHAIR

COUNTING CONUNDRUM

x = 16

\+ = 16

− = 6

(÷) + = ?

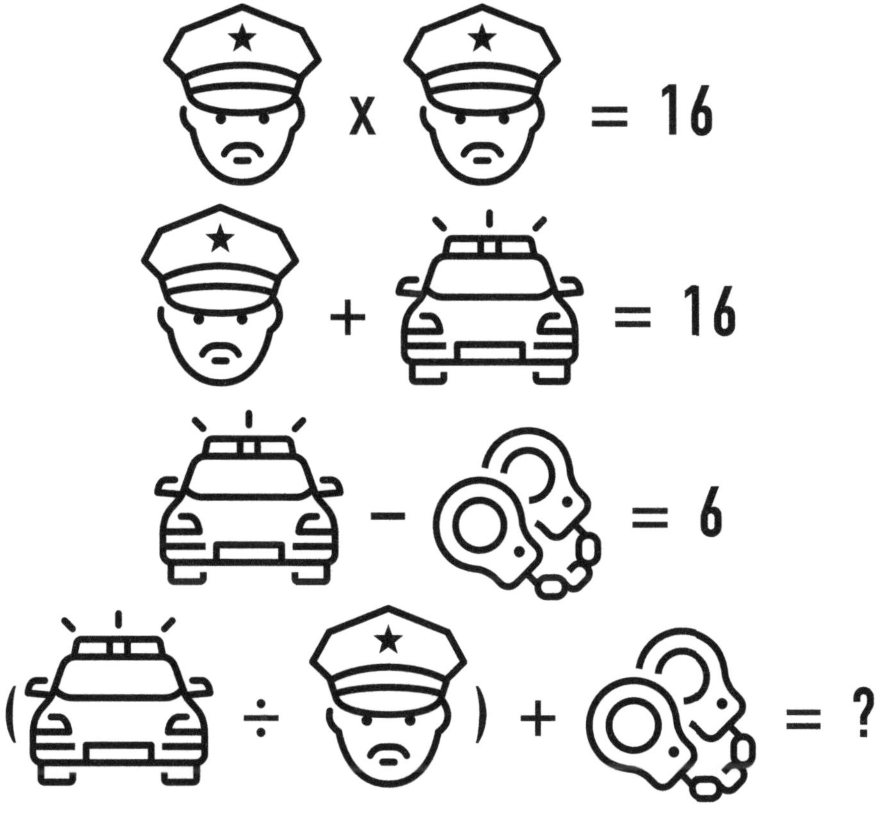

GET THE VALUABLES TO THE MAGIC TRUNK

In the 1780s, an Austrian woman called Barbara Erni performed a brilliant scam. Travelling around Lichtenstein, Germany and beyond, she would arrive at inns and ask that her large trunk be stored wherever the owners stored their valuables. When the coast was clear, an accomplice hidden inside would then creep out and steal everything of value.

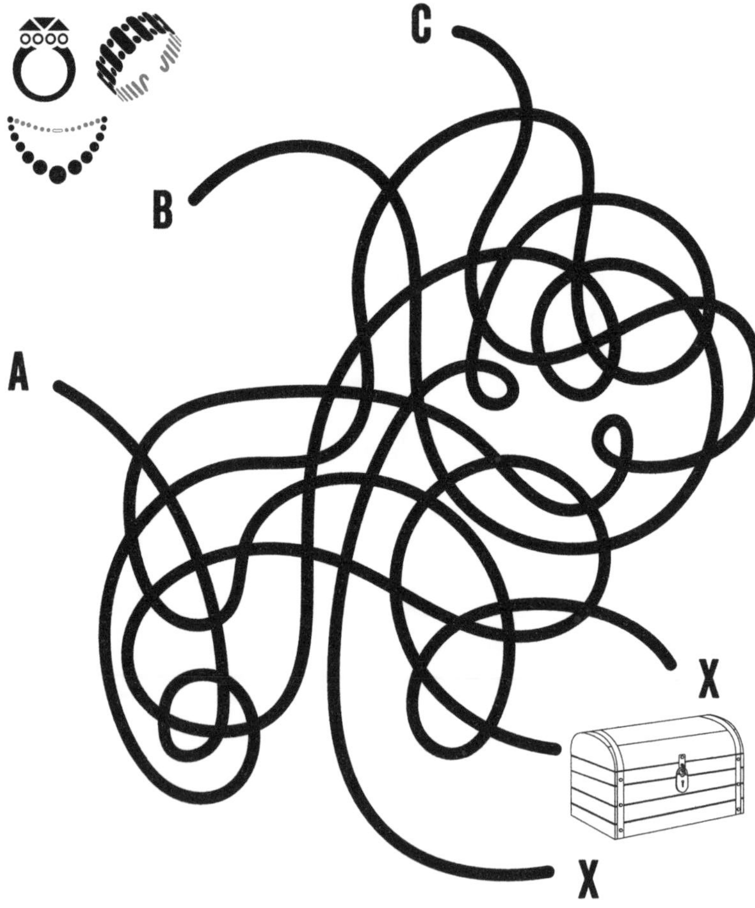

C

B

A

X

X

BETWEEN THE LINES

A word meaning extortion or demanding money with threats can be inserted in the blank line so that, reading downwards, nine three-letter words are formed. What is the hidden word between the lines?

E	S	O	A	S	A	C	B	O
B	Y	T	E	Y	P	R	D	D

In the 1980s, Griselda Blanco was also known by her nickname La Madrina. She was a notorious criminal, famed for her links with organized crime. Which description fits her best?

A. A fraudster nun from Venezuela

B. A billionaire female drug boss from Colombia

C. The owner of a network of brothels in the Philippines

HIDDEN WORD

Can you find the nine-letter word that describes an item sometimes used in kidnappings hidden in the grid?

D	B	L
I	L	O
D	F	N

Complete the following grid by filling in the empty boxes with the missing numbers. Each number can only appear once in a row, column or box.

5		2	1	6	9	3	7	
4	3		2	8	5			
6	1	9	3	4		5	2	8
	5	8		3	2			
9	2	3	4		6	7	8	5
1	4		7		8	2		3
2	7	5	8	9		1	4	
					4	9		2
3		4		2	1	8		7

ACROSTICS

Solve the clues correctly and the shaded squares will reveal a type of robbery.

1. Collide violently
2. Happy facial expression
3. Elsewhere when crime take place
4. Fraudulent schemes
5. Joint connecting hand to arm

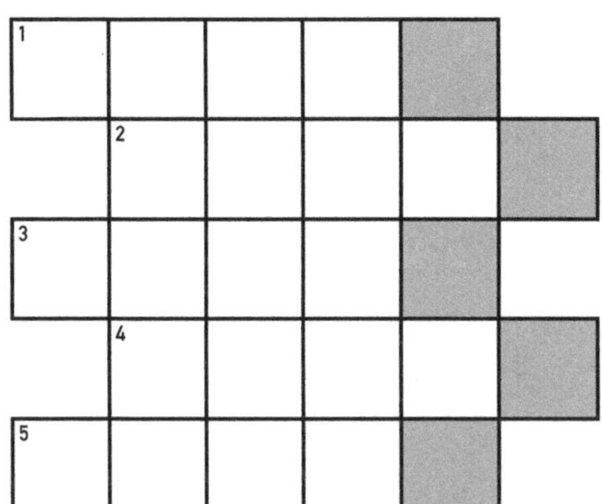

___ ___ ___ ___ ___

ANAGRAMS

Rearrange these letters to reveal three types of cybercrime.

HIGH PINS

_ _ _ _ _ _ _ _

MISS NIGH

_ _ _ _ _ _ _ _

WARM ALE

_ _ _ _ _ _ _

WORDSEARCH

THE GREAT ENIGMA

The theft of Leonardo da Vinci's *Mona Lisa* caused a media sensation in 1911. It took two years for the police to find the culprit: an Italian named Vincenzo Peruggia. Having smuggled the painting out, he travelled to Italy with the painting hidden in a trunk.

Put your investigative skills to work to find the following list of words in the wordsearch.

X	O	R	I	W	S	G	H	T	E	S	R	U	I	E
Z	E	L	I	P	I	U	S	R	C	S	W	G	C	L
Y	O	W	U	N	W	I	M	E	N	M	J	P	N	I
Z	I	C	E	E	R	P	A	L	E	O	Y	U	I	M
L	X	K	T	A	Y	P	A	A	R	C	X	L	V	S
Y	O	Y	P	B	B	J	D	E	O	K	E	T	A	C
N	M	U	Q	L	K	M	N	D	L	X	D	E	D	I
T	Q	J	H	N	P	U	O	T	F	J	Z	Q	O	T
L	J	Q	U	X	D	V	C	R	M	X	W	E	D	A
O	V	R	K	U	M	A	O	A	U	K	R	S	R	M
H	T	P	V	G	W	U	I	R	V	V	I	A	A	G
Y	J	C	G	R	D	F	G	U	U	Z	D	S	N	I
H	J	J	H	A	S	O	A	O	N	I	A	W	O	N
B	L	Q	E	F	W	I	L	E	B	N	H	W	E	E
O	C	J	T	L	D	A	F	A	T	J	P	A	L	U

ART DEALER
ENIGMATIC SMILE
FLORENCE
LA GIOCONDA
LEONARDO DA VINCI
LOUVRE
PARIS
SMOCK
TRUNK

WORD WHEEL

See how many words of four or more letters you can make, using each letter only once. Each word must use the central letter. Can you find the word, a branch of forensic science, that uses all of the letters?

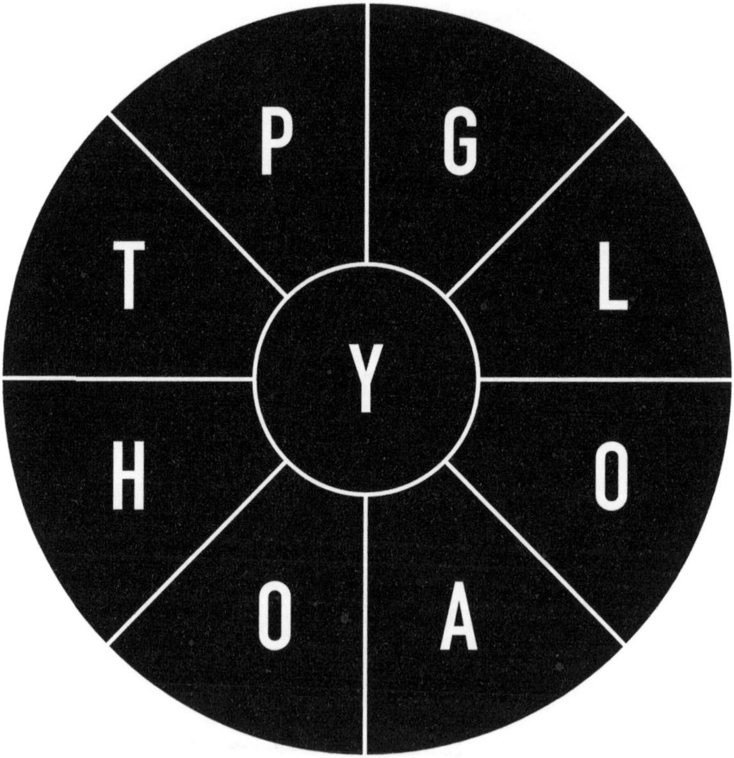

P G L O A O H T

Y

TIARA HEIST

In 2018, the most successful diamond thieves in history, dubbed the Pink Panthers, stole the £3.75 million Portland Tiara by breaking into an armoured glass case at a gallery in Nottinghamshire, UK. They managed to escape but three men were found guilty of the crime in 2022.

Match up the tiaras. The first one has been done for you.

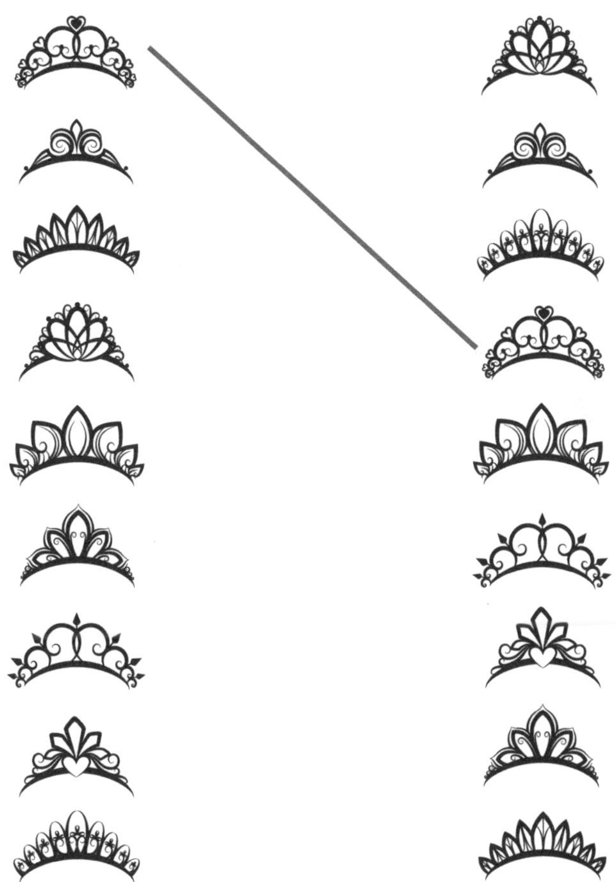

Late one night in 1972, a famous singer accepted a lift in New York. She instantly knew something was wrong when she saw there were no door handles, so she got out quickly by opening the door via an open window. A few years later, she realized the driver had been serial killer Ted Bundy. Who was the singer?

A. Carol Carpenter

B. Cher

C. Debbie Harry

MADE MEN

The Mafia is an organized crime group that originated in Sicily and now operates in the US and Italy. Known by its members as Cosa Nostra ("our thing"), the ruthless criminal activities of the Mafia have featured on big and small screens.

Solve the clues to reveal some of the most popular mafia-inspired movies and TV dramas.

Across

2. Stars Al Pacino and Sharon Stone, also the main attraction of Las Vegas and Monte Carlo (6)
4. Acclaimed 1990 Martin Scorsese movie (10)
5. 1997 movie featuring Johnny Depp (6, 6)
6. First in trilogy about the Corleone family (3, 9)

Down

1. Surname of Tony in TV series, also the highest singing voice of a woman (7)
3. Violent gangster and movie title (8)

WORD WHEEL

See how many words of four or more letters you can make, using each letter only once. Each word must use the central letter. Can you find the word that describes the practice of obtaining something through force and that uses all of the letters?

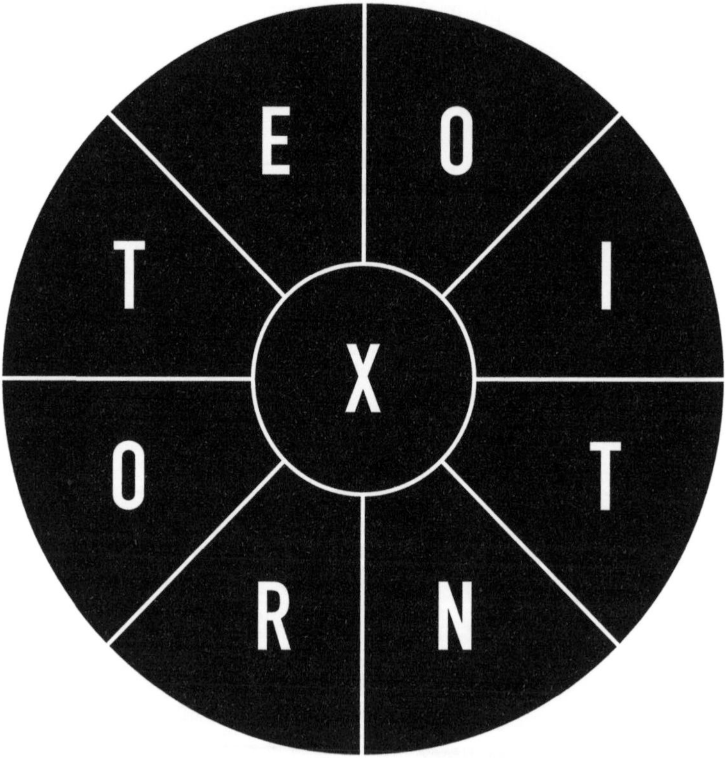

E O

T I

X

O T

R N

CYBERCRIME

With the rise of the internet, cybercrime is now a major global threat. Criminals can hack into secure sites, obtain personal data, steal or demand money and engage in terrorism or espionage.

Can you spot the five differences between the two images below?

GET THE VAN, FILLED WITH GOLD, TO THE SAFE HOUSE

In 1983, six balaclava-wearing robbers broke into the Brink's-Mat warehouse at London's Heathrow Airport. Expecting to find cash worth around £1 million, they instead came across almost 7,000 gold bars alongside a stash of diamonds and money. Loading much of it into their van – a booty worth £26 million – they slipped away, having undertaken one of the biggest gold heists in history.

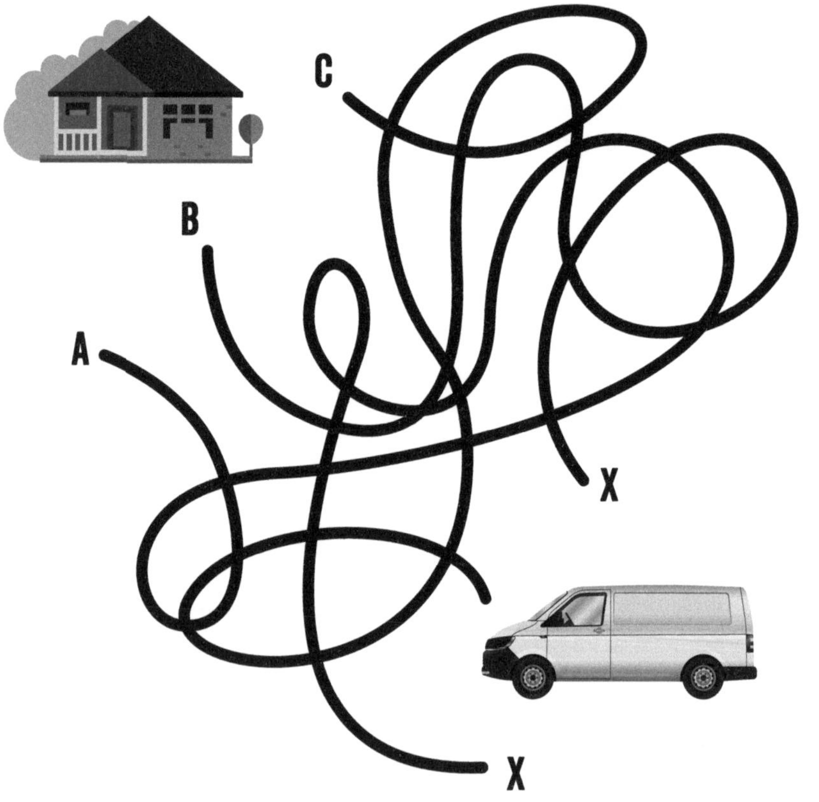

C

B

A

X

X

BETWEEN THE LINES

Someone who might be guilty of a crime can be inserted in the blank line so that, reading downwards, seven three-letter words are formed. What is the hidden word between the lines?

U	B	A	S	K	A	S
E	S	K	Y	Y	E	Y

HIDDEN WORD

Can you find the nine-letter word that describes the practice of obtaining money via deception hidden in the grid?

A	D	U
E	E	D
F	R	R

ANAGRAMS

Poison is the weapon of choice for some serial killers, including the self-named "angel of death" Donald Harvey, who murdered between 37 and 57 people in the 1970s and 1980s. Working as a hospital orderly in Kentucky in the US, his favoured method of murder was to administer poison, either in food or by injection.

Rearrange these letters to reveal three types of poisons.

ACID YEN

_ _ _ _ _ _ _

ACE RINS

_ _ _ _ _ _ _

ITCHY SERNN

_ _ _ _ _ _ _ _ _ _

COUNTING CONUNDRUM

+ = 24

- = 7

x = 20

(÷) x = ?

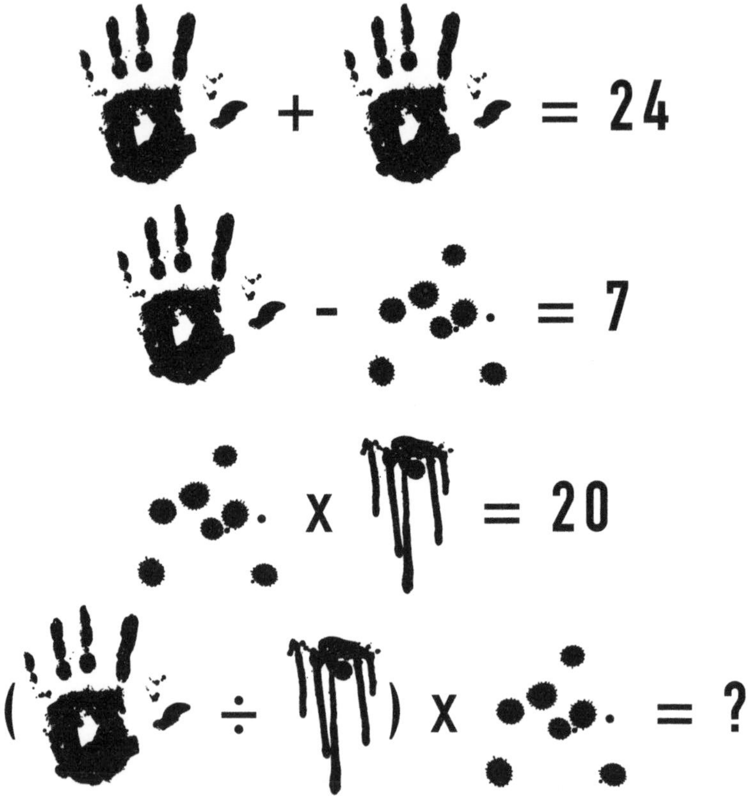

CROSSWORD

CRIME SCENE INVESTIGATORS

The location where a crime takes place, known as the crime scene, will often contain crucial evidence relevant to a criminal investigation. Solve the clues to find the kinds of evidence that crime scene investigators are on the lookout for.

Across

2. Genealogy (5)
6. Published digit (11)

Down

1. Impression of an extremity (9)
3. Strands or follicles (4)
4. Secreted in mouth (6)
5. Garments (8)

Solve the clues correctly and the shaded squares will reveal a person who has committed a crime.

1. To call someone's…
2. A sword, knife or dagger
3. Causing death
4. Trunk of the human body
5. Prolonged warning sound

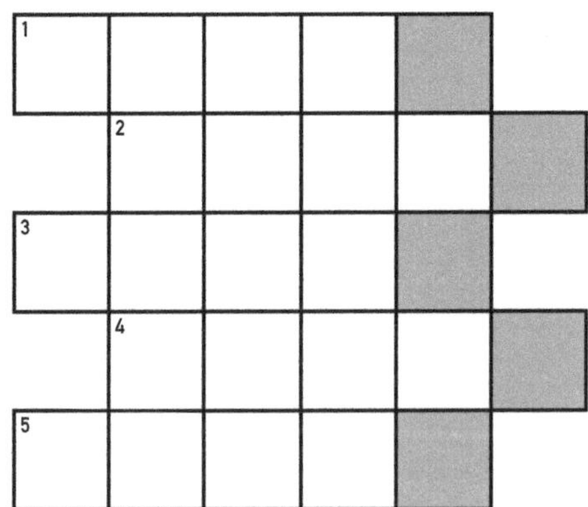

___ ___ ___ ___ ___

MAZE

HELP THE FAIRY REACH THE GIRL

In 1917, photographs of two young girls surrounded by dancing fairies in their garden near Bradford, England shocked the world. For some, it provided proof that fairies and psychic phenomena existed. They became known as the Cottingley Fairies. In the early 1980s, however, the two girls, then in their 70s, admitted the images were faked by using cardboard cut-outs from a book.

BODY SNATCHER

The death of the Macedonian leader Alexander the Great in 323 BCE resulted in a major power struggle between his rivals. During the funeral procession, King Ptolemy I of Egypt seized the body and took it to the city of Alexandria. Alexander's remains, however, have never been found.

Can you spot the five differences between the two images of Alexander the Great?

WORD WHEEL

See how many words of four or more letters you can make, using each letter only once. Each word must use the central letter. Can you find the word meaning a statement given in a court of law that uses all of the letters?

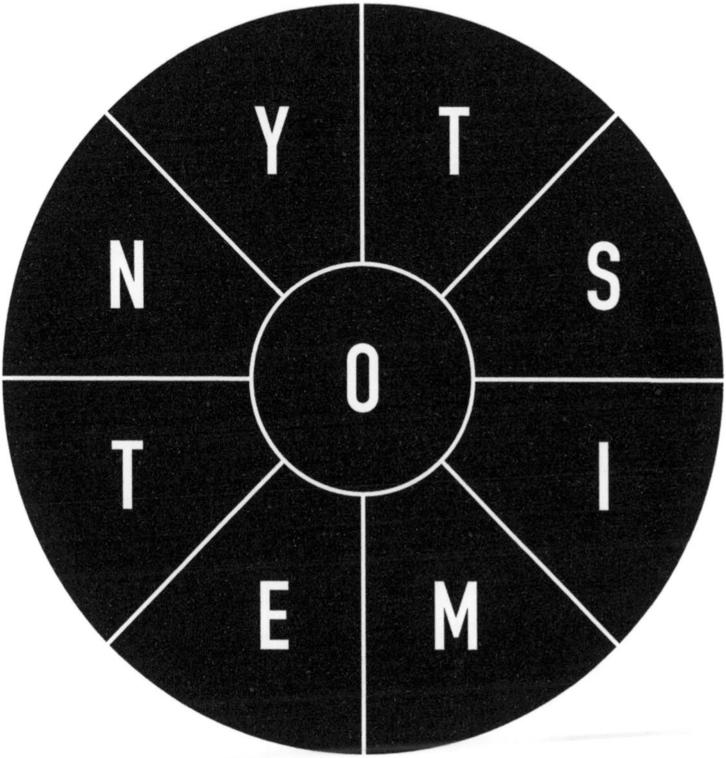

Y T
N S
O
T I
E M

BETWEEN THE LINES

A word for mass murder or wholesale killing can be inserted in the blank line so that, reading downwards, eight three-letter words are formed. What is the hidden word between the lines?

E	C	A	A	B	I	C	P
U	T	K	H	T	E	Y	A

ESCAPE FROM ALCATRAZ

In 1962, three inmates – Clarence Anglin, John Anglin and Frank Morris – escaped the infamous prison on Alcatraz Island, located in San Francisco Bay in the US. Alcatraz housed some of America's most dangerous criminals and the three escapees have never been found or apprehended.

See if you can find some of the items relating to their ingenious escape.

S	M	Y	S	K	G	Y	S	N	O	V	N	E	C	H
Q	L	G	Q	S	W	P	Q	O	S	L	E	O	J	T
G	S	E	M	K	O	A	K	H	B	W	O	Y	F	P
E	J	K	S	O	U	J	L	G	A	H	B	A	J	X
U	W	G	N	I	Z	P	Y	H	Y	R	R	Q	R	L
F	N	S	G	C	H	T	L	R	Y	T	S	F	A	S
P	A	D	D	L	E	C	S	A	F	Q	N	B	I	D
A	J	Z	F	R	N	L	W	I	S	E	N	F	N	A
B	Q	S	D	N	U	F	H	S	W	T	U	M	C	E
L	E	N	N	U	T	S	D	C	X	M	E	K	O	H
E	R	I	W	D	E	B	R	A	B	I	E	R	A	Y
H	V	N	Y	K	S	T	N	S	R	M	X	W	T	O
P	G	E	A	S	I	V	V	O	M	L	G	V	S	C
R	W	M	R	K	X	G	O	W	I	M	Q	K	X	E
M	X	L	C	L	J	C	W	F	U	C	V	L	B	D

BARBED WIRE	MAKESHIFT RAFT	RAINCOATS
CHISELS	PADDLE	SPOONS
DECOY HEADS	PLASTER	TUNNEL

Can you find the nine-letter word that describes the outcome of the death penalty hidden in the grid?

C	T	N
E	O	X
U	I	E

COUNTING CONUNDRUM

− = 12

x = 25

+ = 19

(x) − = ?

Solve the clues correctly and the shaded squares will reveal a type of crime.

1. Pleasant smell
2. Rich house
3. Shine or lustre
4. Goods on ship or vehicle
5. Female ruler

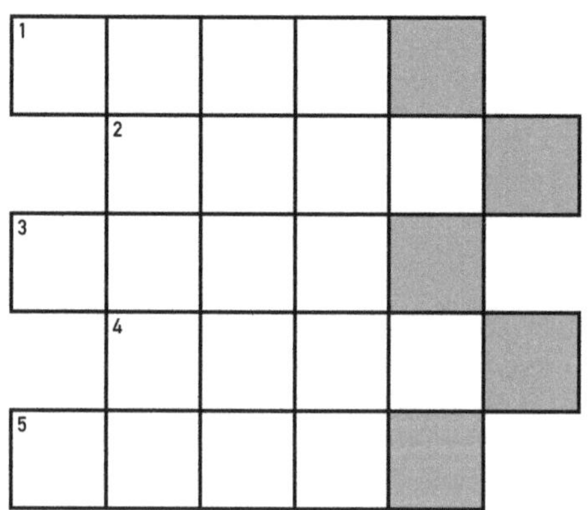

___ ___ ___ ___ ___

What was the nickname for the unidentified American serial killer who spread terror in northern California from the late 1960s to early 1970s? Targeting young couples and a male cab driver, this case has been described as the most famous unsolved murder case in American history.

A. Scorpio

B. The Zodiac Killer

C. The Golden State Killer

Complete the following grid by filling in the empty boxes with the missing numbers. Each number can only appear once in a row, column or box.

2			3	4				7
1	5		7		9		8	2
	7		2	5	8	6	1	
	2	1		8		9	7	5
		8	5			2		
7		5					3	8
8	9	2		3		1		6
6	4	7			5			
			8	2	6	7	4	

 ANAGRAMS

Rearrange these letters to reveal three of the most common illegally trafficked animals around the world.

ERGIT

_ _ _ _ _

GALOP GIN

_ _ _ _ _ _ _ _

HEEL PANT

_ _ _ _ _ _ _ _

THE GREAT TRAIN ROBBERY

In 1963, a gang of armed criminals boarded a train en route to London. They managed to unload 120 sacks of money, amounting to a staggering £2.6 million. The raid had been meticulously planned and shocked the nation.

Match up the trains. The first one has been done for you.

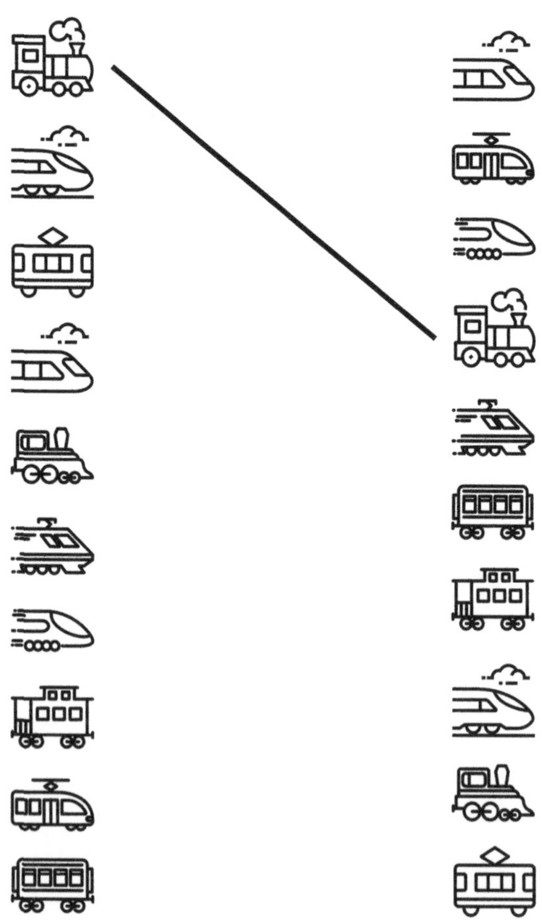

HIDDEN WORD

Can you find the nine-letter word meaning an accomplice hidden in the grid?

Y	C	R
S	O	S
A	C	E

HELP THE HELICOPTER LAND ON THE ROOFTOP

In 2009, robbers in a stolen Bell 206 helicopter landed on the rooftop of a G4S cash service depot in Västerberga, southern Stockholm, Sweden. They then smashed a reinforced window with a sledgehammer, loaded bags of money into the helicopter and took off again. Seven men were later sentenced to prison in connection with the robbery.

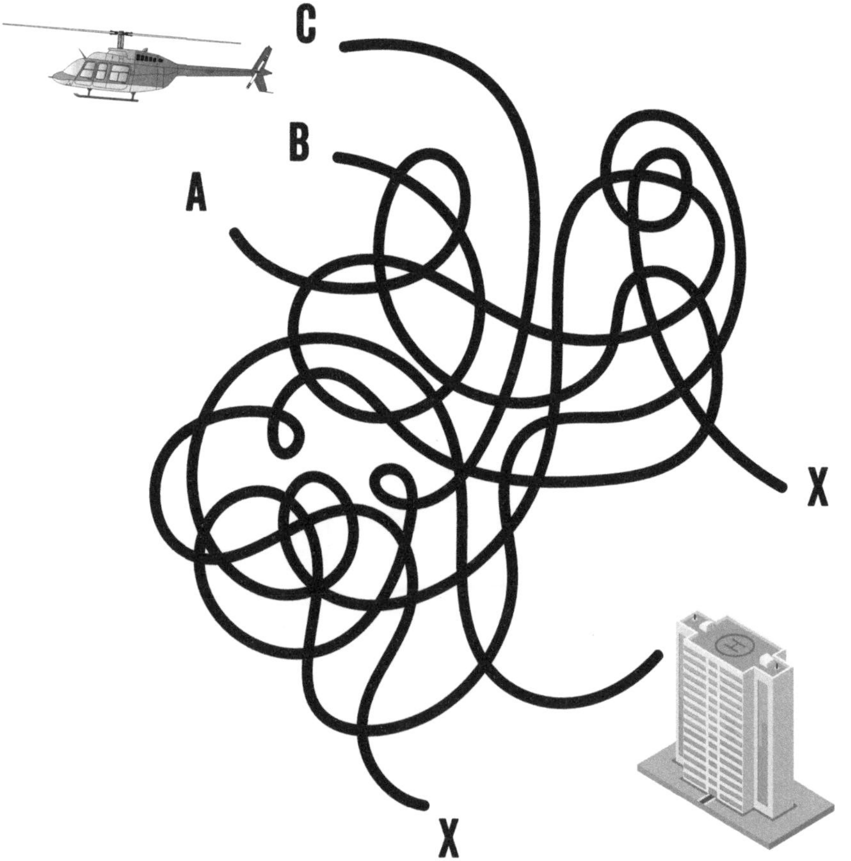

C

B

A

X

X

COUNTING CONUNDRUM

x = 25

x = 30

– = 9

(–) x = ?

BETWEEN THE LINES

A word for someone who ruthlessly preys on or exploits others can be inserted in the blank line so that, reading downwards, eight three-letter words are formed. What is the hidden word between the lines?

S	A	W	A	M	S	T	E
Y	E	D	D	N	Y	Y	A

AGAINST THE ODDS

Around the globe, horse racing and betting are major money-making industries, so it's important to keep the competition fair and regulated. In 2021, racehorse "Medina Spirit" won the Kentucky Derby, though it later failed a drug test. Over 40 years, more than 30 horses from this particular trainer have failed drug tests, with five in that year alone.

Match up the racehorses and their jockeys. The first one has been done for you.

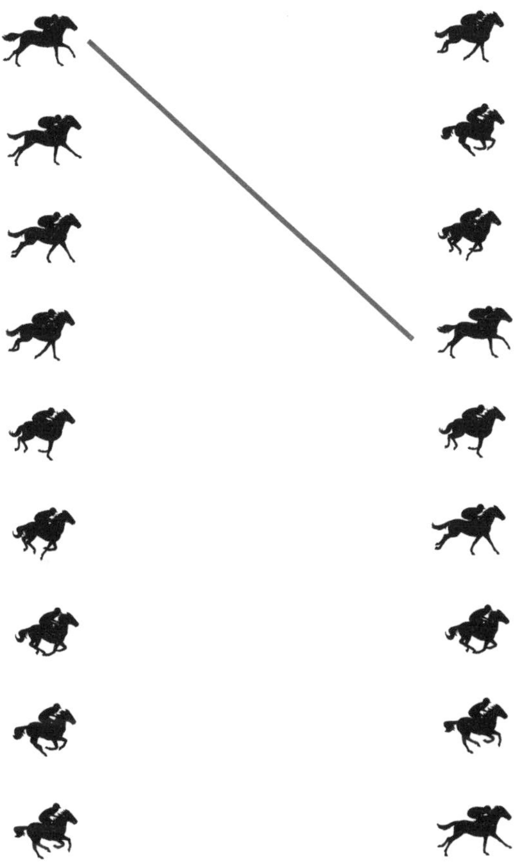

KING OF COCAINE

Pablo Escobar was a notorious Colombian drug lord and the leader of the famous Medellín Cartel. He monopolized the cocaine trade in the US and became one of the richest people in the world. He was eventually killed by police at the age of 44.

See if you can sniff out the words below relating to the man dubbed "the King of Cocaine".

L	T	O	R	X	H	A	K	K	G	O	N	N	L	H
S	E	L	O	P	A	N	A	D	N	E	I	C	A	H
W	V	I	D	F	Q	O	E	V	I	G	M	A	T	A
L	A	R	D	E	T	A	C	A	L	N	W	E	I	S
G	X	K	C	X	C	C	D	T	G	I	Q	I	P	S
Z	E	M	V	U	Q	F	I	B	G	P	M	W	A	A
K	A	J	O	O	Z	G	R	T	U	P	M	W	C	S
C	W	S	I	Q	B	R	N	C	M	A	N	D	R	S
Z	N	I	L	L	E	D	E	M	S	N	B	O	E	I
D	O	W	V	S	F	P	W	S	R	D	J	Q	D	N
D	U	W	Q	J	X	U	L	R	A	I	I	O	R	A
V	M	I	F	O	A	G	G	U	B	K	F	A	U	T
D	S	K	E	B	F	D	O	L	I	X	Y	U	M	I
Z	D	N	U	T	H	D	R	I	O	N	E	G	R	O
R	N	J	E	I	R	E	G	A	N	E	M	R	D	N

ASSASSINATION
HACIENDA NAPOLES
KIDNAPPING
LA CATEDRAL
MEDELLIN
MENAGERIE
MURDER CAPITAL
RIONEGRO
SMUGGLING

In 2007, a northern European country was attacked by an elaborate system of cyber warfare as a result of a disagreement with Russia about the relocation of war memorials and graves in the city of Tallinn. Which country was affected?

A. Estonia

B. Belarus

C. Moldova

ACROSTICS

Solve the clues correctly and the shaded squares will reveal the official at the helm of a law court.

1. Spanish red wine
2. Centre of interest or fixed point
3. Large black and white mammal
4. Code word for the letter T
5. Defamation or slander

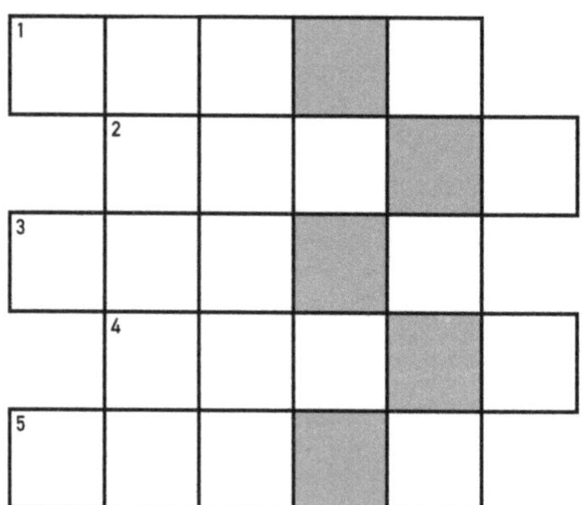

___ ___ ___ ___ ___

WORD WHEEL

See how many words of four or more letters you can make, using each letter only once. Each word must use the central letter. Can you find the word meaning kidnapping that uses all of the letters?

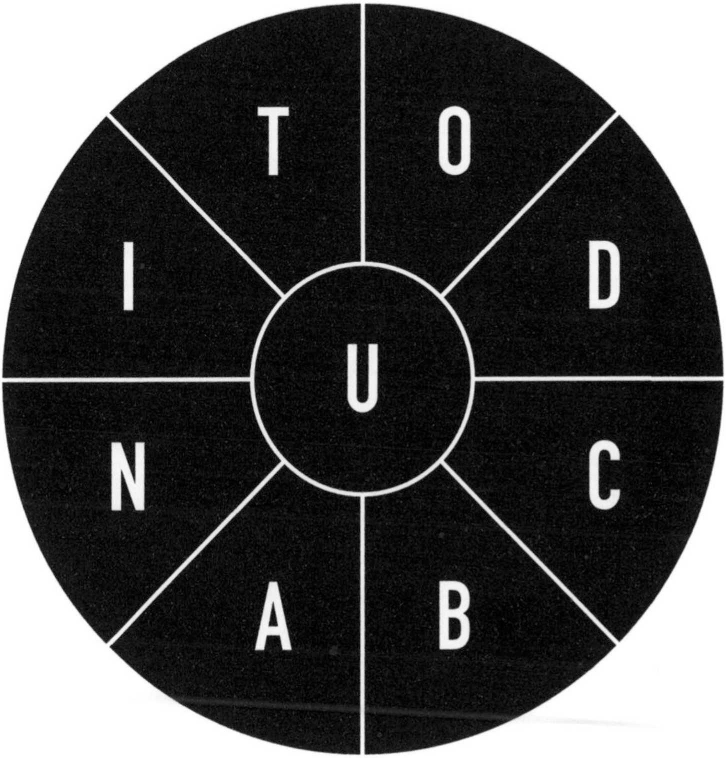

T O D C B A N I

U

Can you find the nine-letter phrase meaning lawsuit hidden in the grid?

C	T	S
A	R	O
E	U	C

THE AXEMAN OF NEW ORLEANS

From May 1918 to October 1919, a serial killer stalked the streets of New Orleans, Louisiana, and the surrounding communities. The killer viciously attacked his victims with an axe, leaving them either dead or hideously wounded. The killer was never identified.

Solve the clues below to reveal more about the brutal attacks.

Across

1. Type of motivation thought to have been behind the attacks (6)
3. Number of murdered victims (3)
6. Organized crime gang suspected of being involved (3, 5)

Down

2. Common carpentry tool used by the killer to break into houses (6)
4. The Mediterranean country of origin for many of the killer's victims (5)
5. Shaving tool used by the killer to slash his victims (5)

SUDOKU

Complete the following grid by filling in the empty boxes with the missing numbers. Each number can only appear once in a row, column or box.

	8	7		4				2
				8	9	1	3	
				2	7	4		
		3	2	9	4		5	
2	5		1		8		7	4
		8	7		6	2		
			8		5	6		9
	6			1		3	8	
8	4	5	9	6	3		2	

ANAGRAMS

Rearrange these letters to reveal words or phrases related to the criminal organization known as the Mafia.

DEAM NAM

_ _ _ _ _ _ _ _

CHAWK

_ _ _ _ _

SOAC ANSTRO

_ _ _ _ _ _ _ _ _ _

BETWEEN THE LINES

A type of proof can be inserted in the blank line so that, reading downwards, eight three-letter words are formed. What is the hidden word between the lines?

T	E	G	O	B	A	I	L
N	E	N	D	D	D	Y	T

WORD WHEEL

See how many words of four or more letters you can make, using each letter only once. Each word must use the central letter. Can you find the word meaning a person with extreme antisocial behaviours that uses all of the letters?

A O P O C I T S

H

HELP THE PRISONER ESCAPE

Dubbed "the man that no prison could hold" Yoshie Shiratori is Japan's most famous prison escapee. First imprisoned in 1936, he went on to escape four times using a variety of inventive methods. These included picking his cell lock with a wire, scaling the walls of his cell and climbing through an air vent, and using a food bowl to dig his way out.

Can you help track the prisoner's escape route?

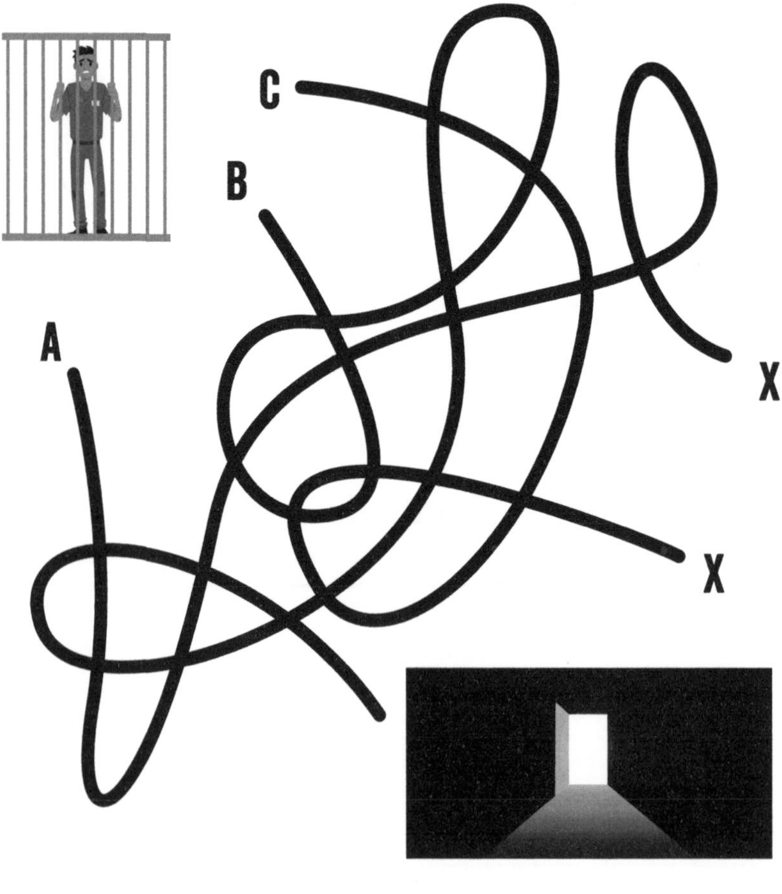

C

B

A

X

X

ACROSTICS

Solve the clues correctly and the shaded squares will reveal a type of white-collar crime.

1. Worn around the neck
2. A person who treads the boards
3. African equine
4. Farewell
5. Tricked

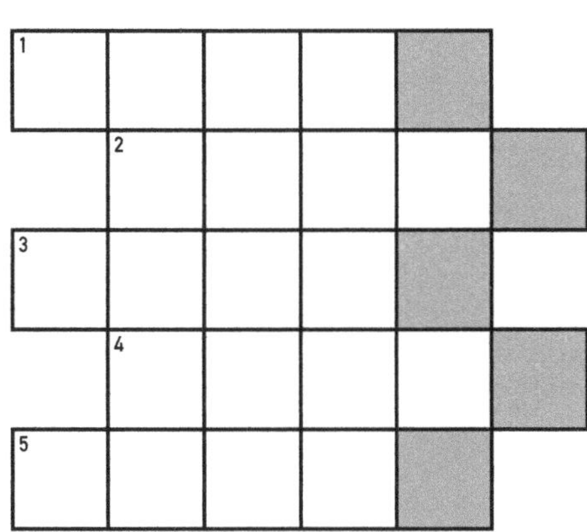

___ ___ ___ ___ ___

How many people have been named as suspects of Jack the Ripper, the serial killer who terrorized the Whitechapel area of London in the late 1880s?

A. 10

B. 100

C. 300

CRIMINAL BEGINNINGS

Many of the words and phrases we use today have their origins in crimes from the past. Solve the clues to reveal some of the phrases and words relating to historic crimes.

Across

5. Being overcharged is like being held up on the road at gunpoint (7, 7)

Down

1. Sweet English girl murdered in 1867 (5, 5)
2. First used in Scotland in the fifteenth century when a murderer was caught with blood on their fingers (9)
3. Object-shaped investment scheme first used in the US in the 1880s through the "Ladies' Deposit" (7)
4. The front seat of a stagecoach was where the weapon wielding guard would sit (7)
6. Parents might read this Act (4)

SERIAL KILLERS

A serial killer is typically a person who murders more than three people. The motivation behind their terrible crimes varies. Some derive pleasure, excitement or sexual gratification from murder, while others seek to exert power over their victims.

See if you can find the names or nicknames of some of the world's most notorious serial killers.

J	P	U	Z	H	D	Z	S	K	L	Q	G	G	X	W
E	E	Q	Q	J	T	N	O	N	E	T	B	R	V	Y
F	D	U	S	B	V	L	N	R	G	E	N	N	S	I
F	R	E	K	R	P	D	R	D	Ö	F	B	O	K	D
R	O	Q	P	V	K	H	O	X	H	X	T	L	N	L
E	L	T	R	K	O	Z	U	M	S	S	F	H	A	M
Y	Ó	E	Z	R	R	X	W	M	L	Y	N	S	M	S
D	P	D	O	Z	W	T	N	J	E	L	P	L	E	G
A	E	B	H	V	D	B	E	N	I	E	E	M	N	L
H	Z	U	F	S	E	A	E	G	N	N	L	M	O	V
M	J	N	Z	F	E	Q	L	T	V	O	E	O	T	L
E	K	D	H	Y	Z	C	I	S	H	R	E	G	S	M
R	S	Y	P	G	X	U	A	H	L	K	Z	A	E	N
H	A	R	O	L	D	S	H	I	P	M	A	N	H	F
V	O	K	P	O	P	L	I	A	H	K	I	M	T	F

AILEEN WUORNOS
H. H. HOLMES
HAROLD SHIPMAN
JEFFREY DAHMER
MIKHAIL POPKOV
NIELS HÖGEL
PEDRO LÓPEZ
THE STONEMAN
TED BUNDY

ONE LAST JOB

In 2015, a gang of elderly robbers broke into a safety deposit facility in Hatton Garden, the famous jewellery quarter of London, and made off with millions of pounds' worth of precious gems. The six men, all experienced thieves doing "one last job", used power drills to tunnel into the vault's thick walls.

Match up the gemstones. The first one has been done for you.

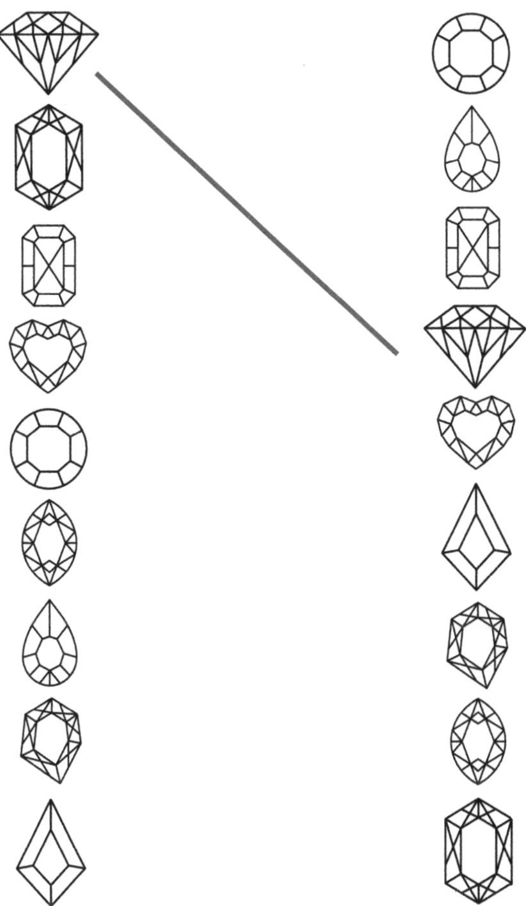

COUNTING CONUNDRUM

CRIME SCENE + CRIME SCENE = 80

CRIME SCENE ÷ = 4

x = 30

(CRIME SCENE +) − = ?

ANAGRAMS

Rearrange these letters to reveal the different methods of execution for criminals sentenced with the death penalty in modern times.

ACETIN JELLO THIN

_ _ _ _ _ _ _ _ _ _ _ _ _ _ _ _ _ _

CALCITE RICHER

_ _ _ _ _ _ _ _ _ _ _ _ _ _ _ _

DRAG IFS QUIN

_ _ _ _ _ _ _ _ _ _ _ _ _ _

THE PARTY THAT NEVER HAPPENED

In April 2017, around 5,000 partygoers bought tickets to attend a luxury music festival on an island in the Bahamas. On arrival, they discovered the headline acts had dropped out and their "luxury" provisions were soaking tents, not villas, and terrible food. The co-creator of Fyre Festival, Billy McFarland, pleaded guilty to fraud.

Can you spot the five differences between the two images?

Jordan Belfort, a former stockbroker born in 1962, pleaded guilty to fraud and crimes related to stock market manipulation as well as running a penny-stock scam. His memoir was made into a film. What was its name?

A. *The Big Short*

B. *Money Monster*

C. *The Wolf of Wall Steet*

GET THE SYRUP TO THE GETAWAY VEHICLE

Across 2011 and 2012, Canada was gripped by the bizarre theft of almost 3,000 tonnes of maple syrup. Around CA$18 million of syrup was gradually removed and spirited away each night. It became known as the Great Canadian Maple Syrup Heist, achieved cult status and has even inspired a comedy drama.

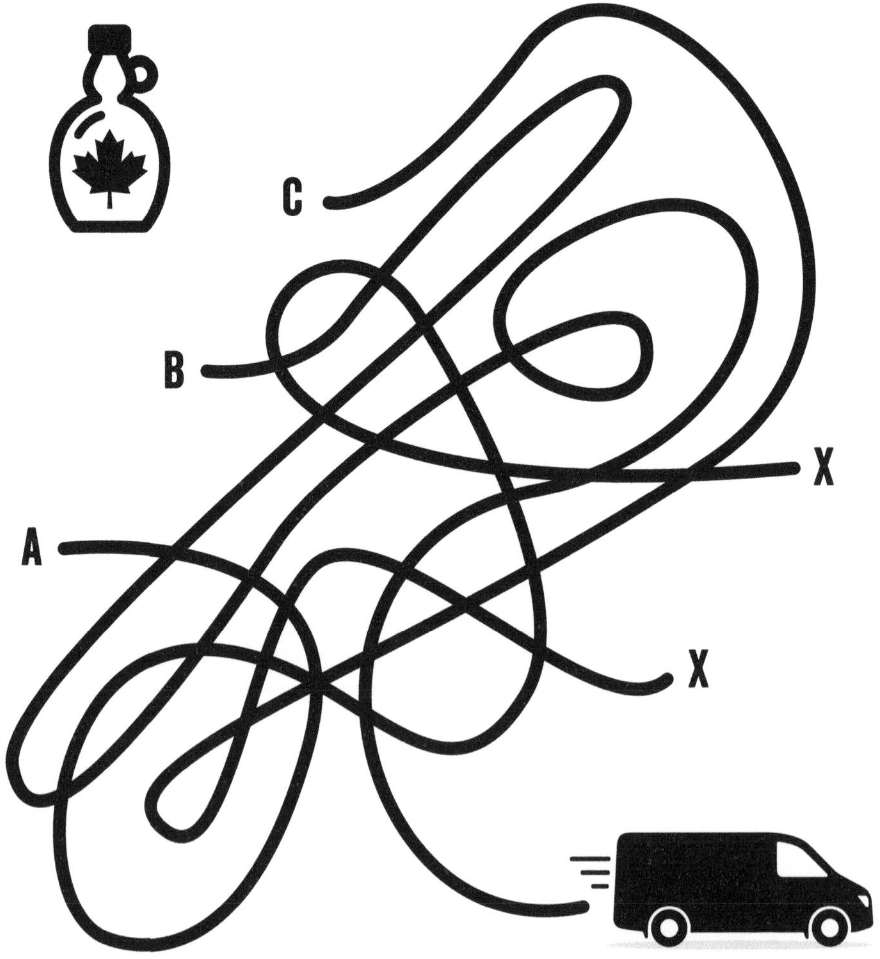

C

B

X

A

X

BETWEEN THE LINES

A word meaning to defraud or cheat someone out of money can be inserted in the blank line so that, reading downwards, seven three-letter words are formed. What is the hidden word between the lines?

A	A	S	E	O	S	G
H	E	N	D	D	Y	M

THE LIZARD KING

In 2010, officials at an airport in Malaysia made an astonishing discovery. A suitcase on the conveyor belt snapped open, and out poured not personal possessions, but snakes. The owner of the suitcase, Wong Keng Liang, was such a prolific animal trafficker that he became known as the "Lizard King".

Match up the snakes. The first one has been done for you.

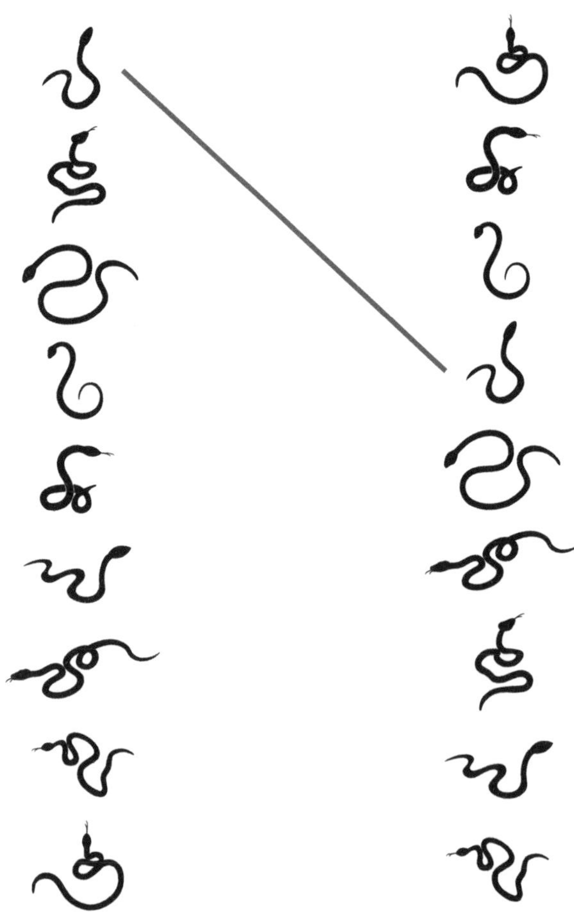

Which well-known name was murdered by a gunman on the steps of his Miami Beach mansion in 1997?

A. Tupac Shakur

B. Gianni Versace

C. Marvin Gaye

COUNTING CONUNDRUM

x = 9

+ = 18

− = 8

(÷) x = ?

WARNING SIGNS

Serial killers can come from all walks of life, but according to experts, there are a few early warning signs or patterns of behaviour that might later lead to their heinous crimes. Solve the clues to reveal what these might be.

Across

4. Sharpness or cleverness (12)
5. Inflicting pain (on an animal) (7)
6. Setting things ablaze (5)

Down

1. Mistreatment as a child (5)
2. Dependency (9)
3. Not a conversationalist (10)

HIDDEN WORD

Can you find the nine-letter word meaning abductor hidden in the grid?

I	R	E
P	A	P
D	N	K

ANAGRAMS

Rearrange these letters to reveal words related to human trafficking.

BLOOD FARCEUR

_ _ _ _ _ _ _   _ _ _ _ _ _

ARM STING

_ _ _ _ _ _ _ _ _

GERM SLUGS

_ _ _ _ _ _ _ _ _ _

KAYAKING FRAUDSTER

In 2002, John Darwin set out on his kayak from the seaside town of Seaton Carew in the UK's County Durham. He disappeared, but five years later he turned up in London claiming to have amnesia. Police discovered his disappearance was all part of an insurance scam, and in 2008, he and his wife were sentenced to prison.

Can you spot the five differences between the two images below?

SUDOKU

Complete the following grid by filling in the empty boxes with the missing numbers. Each number can only appear once in a row, column or box.

		7	2	8	1			5
5				7		9	3	1
6	1			3			2	
				1	8	3	5	6
8				6	3	1		
	6	3		5		8		
	3			9			8	
9	5	1			7	2	6	
7		6	3			4	1	9

ACROSTICS

Solve the clues correctly and the shaded squares will reveal a murder weapon.

1. Often with mirrors
2. Extreme anguish
3. Keep away from
4. Larceny
5. Group of twelve

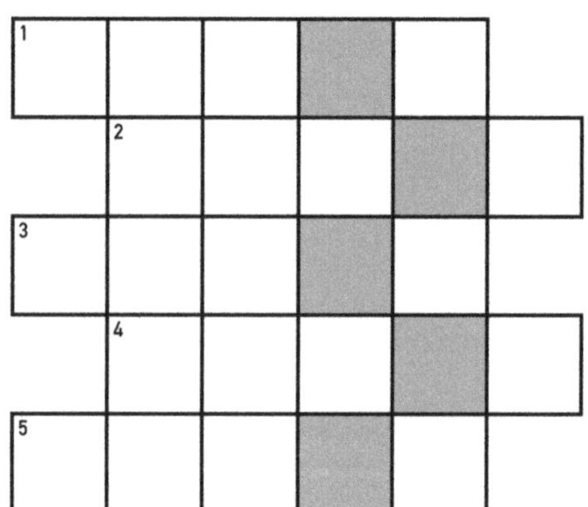

___ ___ ___ ___ ___

WHITECHAPEL BUTCHER

The unidentified serial killer Jack the Ripper terrorized London in the 1880s, murdering at least five women who were working as prostitutes in the slums of the East End. The killings were particularly brutal as Jack the Ripper slit his victims' throats and mutilated their bodies, cutting out their reproductive organs.

Can you find the words and names relating to one of England's most famous criminals?

J M N Y P M G R X A M I R G D
L A A V O Y P E A A S B Q S I
O R M R O U U T A N N L S C S
D Y P Z K K Y T J I E P N O E
G A A F N F A E Q B I W O T M
I N H R I E I L P T H R R L B
N N C X H J N L A I V S P A O
G N E J M Z G L T Q U A A N W
H I I T U T F E M V P J R D E
O C N D V I C H B C O F E Y L
U H N V E H P M P P N I H A L
S O A L A H J O L L G A T R E
E L D P N O A R L C W C A D D
S S E R F X L F R I P T E G S
K L F T I N M B X P L R L L A

ANNIE CHAPMAN	FROM HELL LETTER	SCOTLAND YARD
DISEMBOWELLED	LODGING HOUSES	SPITALFIELDS
LEATHER APRON	MARY ANN NICHOLS	WHITECHAPEL

WORD WHEEL

See how many words of four or more letters you can make, using each letter only once. Each word must use the central letter. Can you find the word meaning destruction of property that uses all of the letters?

A M
S I
L
N A
D V

BETWEEN THE LINES

A post-mortem examination can be inserted in the blank line so that, reading downwards, seven three-letter words are formed. What is the hidden word between the lines?

B	C	S	T	S	U	D
T	T	Y	E	Y	E	E

Rearrange these letters to reveal words or phrases related to criminal acts and money.

MENU OH SHY

_ _ _ _ _ _ _ _ _ _

ACT BALM KERK

_ _ _ _ _ _ _ _ _ _ _ _

FRILLY CHUTE

_ _ _ _ _ _ _ _ _ _ _

FRENCH FRAUDSTER

Victor Lustig was a notorious con artist of the early twentieth century, who operated scams and get-rich-quick schemes across the US and Europe. In the 1920s he even convinced wealthy scrap metal merchants to buy the iconic monument of Paris, the Eiffel Tower – a brazen scheme that he attempted twice!

Can you spot the five differences between the two images?

HELP THE POLICE CAR CATCH O. J. SIMPSON'S BRONCO

In 1994, Orenthal "O. J." Simpson led police on a 60-mile car chase through southern California. The event happened just two days after the brutal murders of his ex-wife, Nicole Brown Simpson, and her friend, Ron Goldman. The chase ended in Simpson's arrest, although he was later acquitted of their murder in a heavily publicized trial.

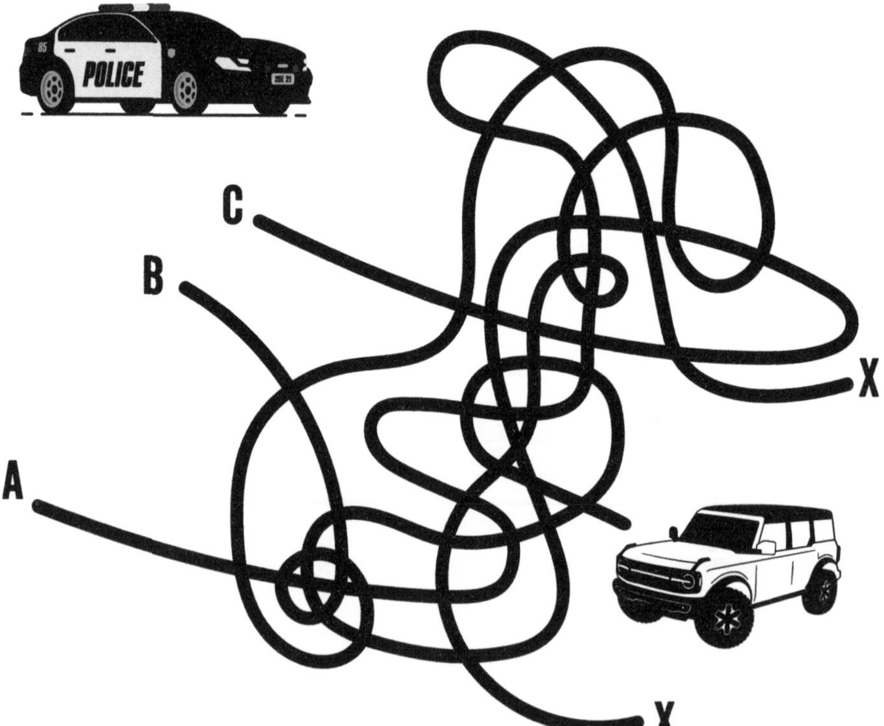

C

B

X

A

X

In July 1918, during the Russian Revolution, Tsar Nicholas II, his wife Alexandra Romanov and their six children were executed by firing squad. In the following years, rumours circulated that a family member had escaped. Several women claimed to be the mysterious royal, although DNA evidence in 2007 proved that she had been murdered alongside her family. Which Romanov was it?

A. Alexandra Romanov

B. Maria Romanov

C. Anastasia Romanov

COUNTING CONUNDRUM

 x  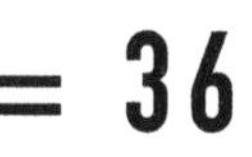 = 36

 x  = 60

 +  = 31

( + ) −  = ?

BANK JOBS

A crime wave swept through Germany in 2022 when nearly 500 ATM bank machines were attacked by robbers. They blew up the machines using powerful explosives and seized the banknotes from the rubble before making a quick getaway.

Match up the bombs. The first one has been done for you.

WORD WHEEL

See how many words of four or more letters you can make, using each letter only once. Each word must use the central letter. Can you find the word for a series of scientific tests that uses all of the letters?

R N S O C I E S

F

CROSSWORD

THE TRIADS

The Triads are organized crime groups based in China and in some countries across the world with Chinese communities. They are involved in various criminal activities from drug trafficking to illegal gambling. Members participate in initiation rituals and adhere to codes of conduct.

Solve the clues to reveal other facts associated with the Triads.

Across

3. Gambling haven off Hong Kong (5)
5. Major trade in this drug (6)
6. Californian city known for its Chinatown (3, 9)

Down

1. The bosses of the Triads are named after this mythical reptile's cranium (10)
2. Japanese version of the Triads (6)
4. A crime gang in China named after a large shape (3, 6)

Solve the clues correctly and the shaded squares will reveal a word for a period of unrestrained activity, particularly relating to a "shooting ______"

1. Kings and queens play this game
2. Opium flower
3. Storytelling through music and song
4. Made from nectar
5. Rod or card game

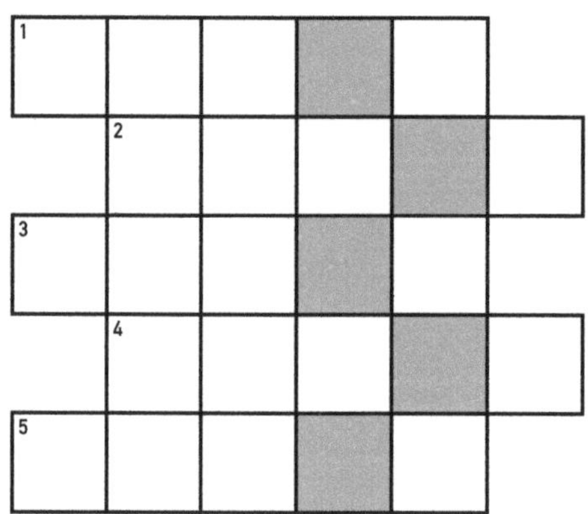

___ ___ ___ ___ ___

COUNTING CONUNDRUM

+ = 34

+ = 42

x = 125

+ + = ?

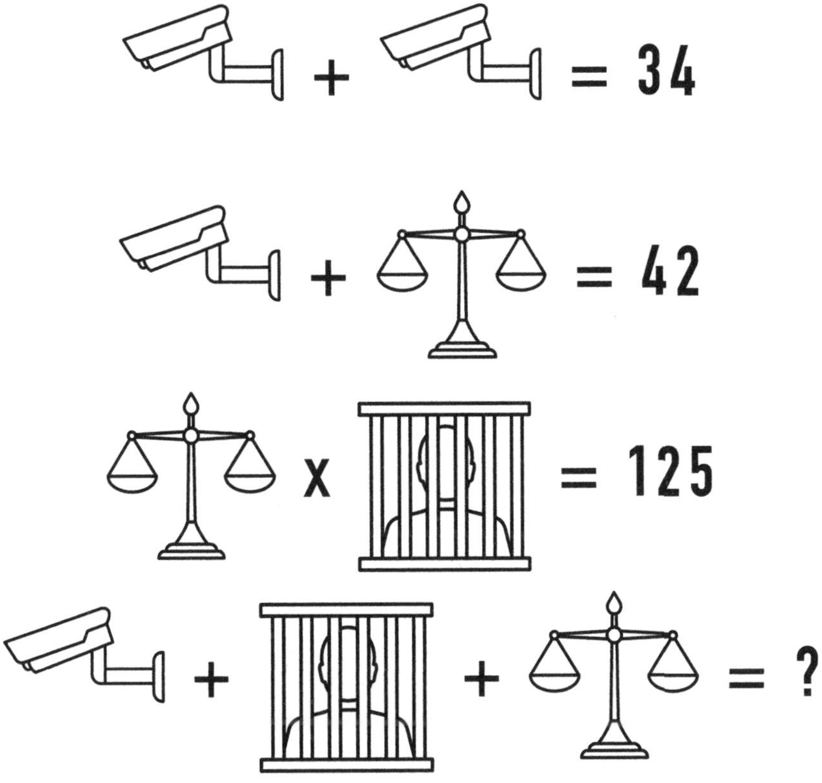

HIDDEN WORD

Can you find the nine-letter word meaning trickery hidden in the grid?

C	O	I
E	N	T
P	E	D

BETWEEN THE LINES

A con artist can be inserted in the blank line so that, reading downwards, seven three-letter words are formed. What is the hidden word between the lines?

T	C	A	A	S	B	E
E	T	K	E	Y	E	R

WORDSEARCH

FAMOUS ASSASSINATIONS

Assassinations, or the planned murders of prominent people, have always attracted huge media attention and speculation. Such public acts of violence can trigger widespread grief, further unrest and, in the case of Archduke Franz Ferdinand in 1914, a world war.

See if you can track down the names of well-known people who were assassinated.

I	H	D	N	A	G	A	M	T	A	H	A	M	W	E
Y	O	F	N	Z	E	D	U	P	Z	B	P	S	K	B
I	S	T	Z	O	F	U	P	A	I	I	A	M	J	A
T	Z	H	T	J	N	Q	F	C	X	M	J	O	U	O
Z	O	B	R	U	M	N	S	P	K	X	H	J	M	Z
H	G	T	U	L	H	V	E	L	R	N	K	J	P	N
A	P	R	H	I	N	B	L	L	F	K	R	B	X	I
K	X	A	D	U	Q	U	R	K	N	P	D	M	H	H
R	M	Q	N	S	N	V	E	I	M	H	L	L	O	S
A	S	G	M	C	S	N	J	N	Z	O	O	R	F	T
B	N	L	E	A	N	B	C	C	C	A	S	J	F	W
I	Q	E	D	E	M	H	M	L	N	H	N	V	G	Z
N	Y	M	D	S	E	V	A	P	S	V	A	E	H	Z
L	Z	Y	P	A	B	M	U	X	R	F	J	A	B	N
I	V	M	H	R	H	B	R	L	I	D	H	Y	J	S

JULIUS CAESAR	JOHN LENNON	YITZHAK RABIN
JOHN F. KENNEDY	SHINZO ABE	BENAZIR BHUTTO
MAHATMA GANDHI	MALCOLM X	ABRAHAM LINCOLN

THE WILD WEST

Henry McCarty, better known as Billy the Kid, was an outlaw, cattle rustler and gunfighter of America's Wild West. He is said to have killed over 20 men before he was convicted in 1881 for three murders and sentenced to be hanged. He escaped jail but was caught and shot. He was only 21 when he died.

Match up the cowboy hats. The first one has been done for you.

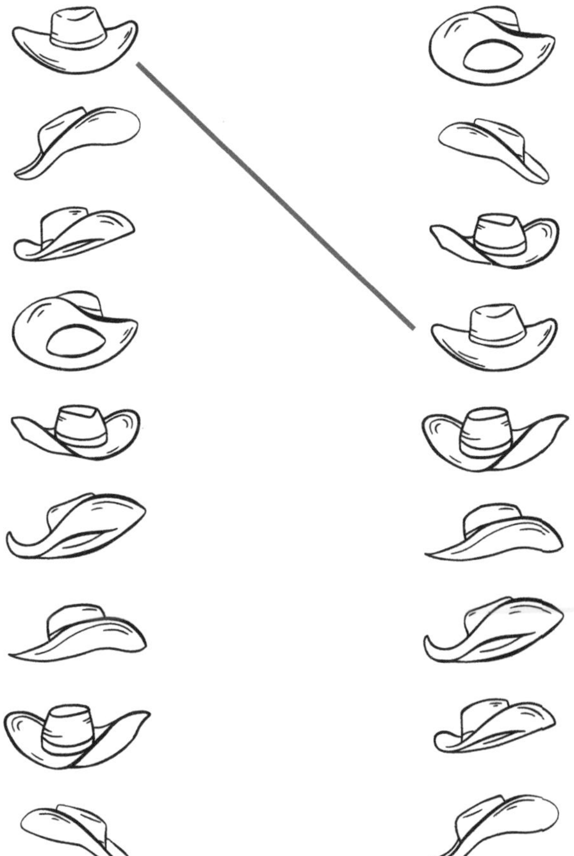

CATCH ME IF YOU CAN

Frank Abagnale is one of the world's most well-known imposters, so much so that his criminal exploits were immortalized in a Steven Spielberg film starring Leonardo DiCaprio. Solve the clues to find the characters Abagnale has claimed to have impersonated.

Across

2. Legal representative (6)
5. Protection, sentry (8, 5)
6. The arm of the law (6, 7)

Down

1. A mentor (7)
3. Highflyer (5)
4. An academic (6)

HELP THE SCAM QUEEN MAKE IT TO THE NIGHTCLUB

Anna Sorokin, otherwise known as Anna Delvey, made headlines in 2018 when she was arrested for posing as a wealthy German heiress in New York. To fund her lavish life, she swindled banks, hotels and individuals out of hundreds of thousands of dollars. She was eventually arrested in 2019 for grand larceny.

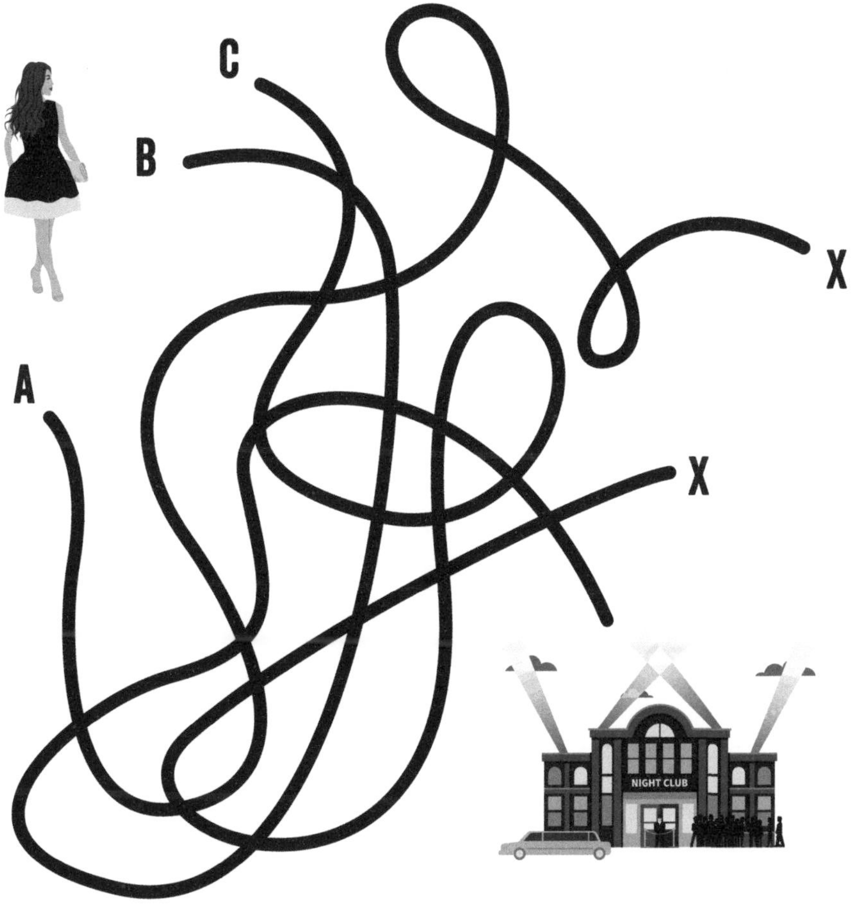

FORENSIC SCIENCE

Scientific forensic techniques are often critical to criminal investigations. They might be used to examine evidence at a crime scene, as part of an autopsy on a body, or to delve into a suspect's digital files.

See if you can track down all the different techniques forensic scientists might employ in a crime investigation.

L	Y	M	Q	K	E	R	T	I	I	K	Y	C	L	Q
C	J	X	L	F	C	W	B	X	M	S	R	N	E	B
M	A	Y	P	O	C	S	O	R	T	C	E	P	S	Y
O	Y	R	X	C	I	N	Q	D	Z	T	W	T	L	R
E	W	F	B	A	L	L	I	S	T	I	C	S	P	O
Y	G	O	L	O	C	I	X	O	T	V	N	D	M	O
L	G	N	I	T	N	I	R	P	R	E	G	N	I	F
O	V	L	S	H	F	D	V	F	L	L	W	E	C	I
N	P	Z	C	U	H	T	A	C	L	R	S	A	R	I
I	T	S	P	R	H	V	H	T	D	J	L	K	O	Q
M	T	Q	L	S	G	M	K	O	I	P	W	I	S	B
U	S	I	S	Y	L	A	N	A	A	N	D	N	C	Q
L	A	T	E	N	T	P	R	I	N	T	G	Y	O	V
R	C	C	S	M	S	K	X	S	P	W	Z	P	P	Q
E	G	U	Y	J	W	A	J	M	M	U	J	P	Y	G

BALLISTICS	FINGERPRINTING	MICROSCOPY
CARBON DATING	LATENT PRINT	SPECTROSCOPY
DNA ANALYSIS	LUMINOL	TOXICOLOGY

In 1996, Martin Bryant went on a shooting spree in Port Arthur, Tasmania, tragically killing 35 people. The horrendous nature of the massacre led to the killer receiving a long sentence in prison, without parole. What was the length of his sentence?

A. 35 life sentences plus 16 years

B. 35 life sentences plus 165 years

C. 35 life sentences plus 1,652 years

THE DIGITAL ERA

With the advent of the internet, the capacity for extortion only increased – and as tech gets more complex, so too do the potential scams. Most of us will have access to a mobile phone, a laptop or a tablet – and will therefore have received phishing emails or mass missives that, with just one click, could lead us to financial ruin.

Can you spot the five differences between the two images?

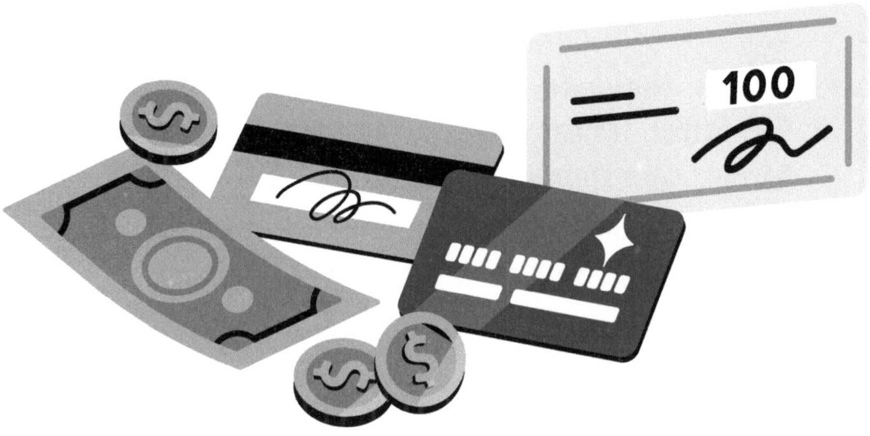

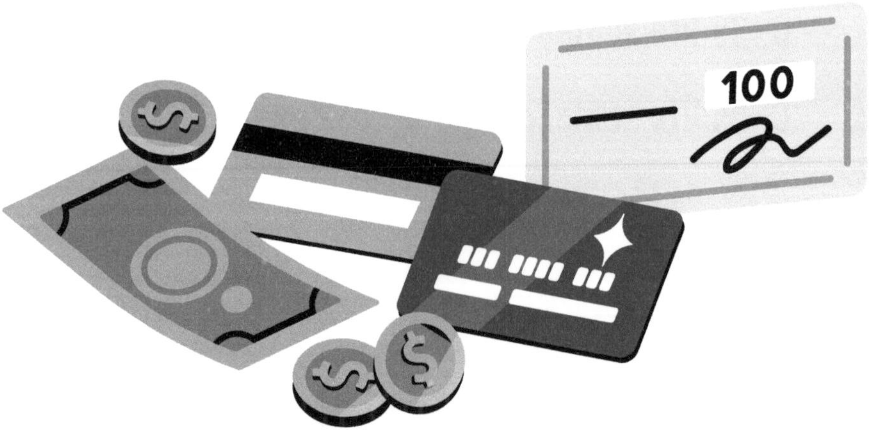

WORD WHEEL

See how many words of four or more letters you can make, using each letter only once. Each word must use the central letter. Can you find the phrase meaning ruthless killing that uses all of the letters?

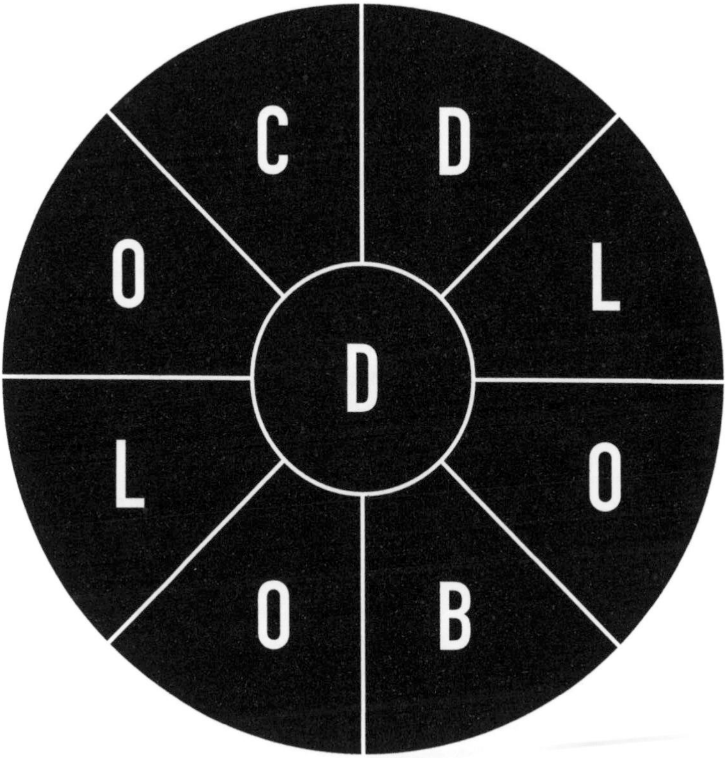

C D

O L

D

L O

O B

HIDDEN WORD

Can you find the nine-letter phrase meaning scammer or swindler hidden in the grid?

S	T	C
I	O	R
T	N	A

ANAGRAMS

Rearrange these letters to reveal three types of serial killers.

RAINY VOIS

_ _ _ _ _ _ _ _ _ _ _

CHIN TODIES

_ _ _ _ _ _ _ _ _ _ _ _

MIOSIS INTERNODE

_ _ _ _ _ _ _ _   _ _ _ _ _ _ _ _ _ _

SCOURGE OF THE SEAS

Sea-faring pirates have been terrorizing the oceans since ancient times. Even Julius Caesar was kidnapped by pirates. The seventeenth and early eighteenth centuries saw a golden age of piracy, and some of the most famous pirates developed a fearsome reputation for capturing ships laden with treasure and attacking coastal towns.

Solve the clues to reveal some well-known names and facts related to piracy.

Across

3. Flame-haired North African pirate (10)
6. Male duck, hero in England and a pirate to the Spanish (7, 5)

Down

1. Spanish dollar and coveted treasure (6, 2, 5)
2. Spanish, treasure-laden ship (7)
4. Fearsome, dark-haired English pirate (10)
5. Pirate flag (5, 5)

AN ELEGANT RUSE

The Forty Elephants were an all-female shoplifting gang operating in the Elephant and Castle area of Victorian London. Most famously, they gained entry to Selfridges by posing as high-class ladies and made off with an enormous theft of jewels and clothing.

Can you spot the five differences between the two images?

MAGIC KEY

In early 1995, three men (two murderers and one arsonist) escaped a prison on the Isle of Wight in the UK by using a "magic key" they had made in the prison's metal shop. They had also made a steel ladder so they could scale the prison wall.

Match up the keys. The first has been done for you.

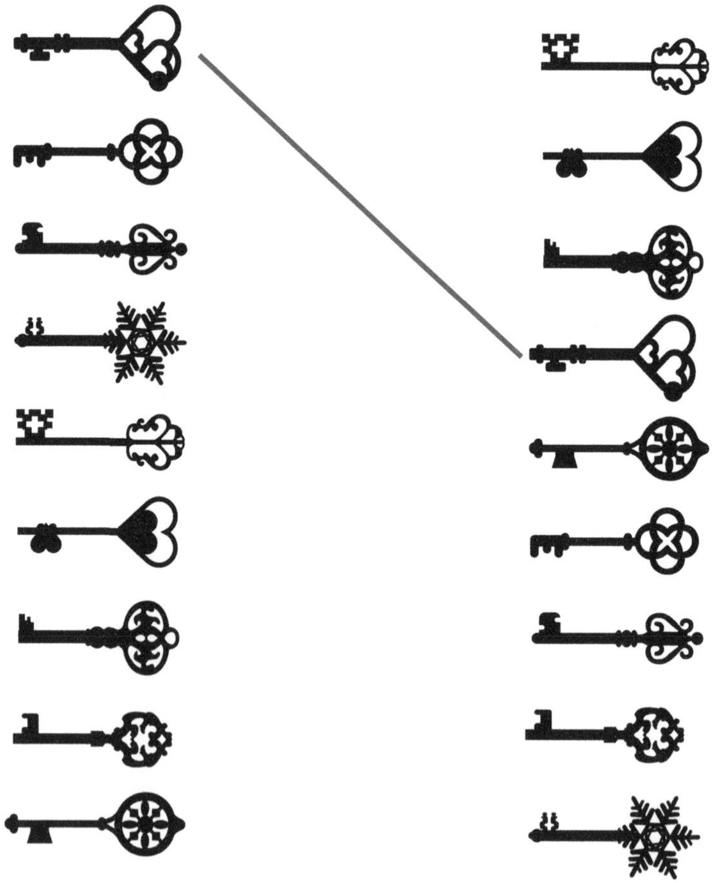

ACROSTICS

Solve the clues correctly and the shaded squares will reveal a type of circumstantial evidence.

1. Bean or butter
2. Guttural noise
3. A digital icon used to express emotion
4. A plant with a rounded shape
5. A spicy pepper

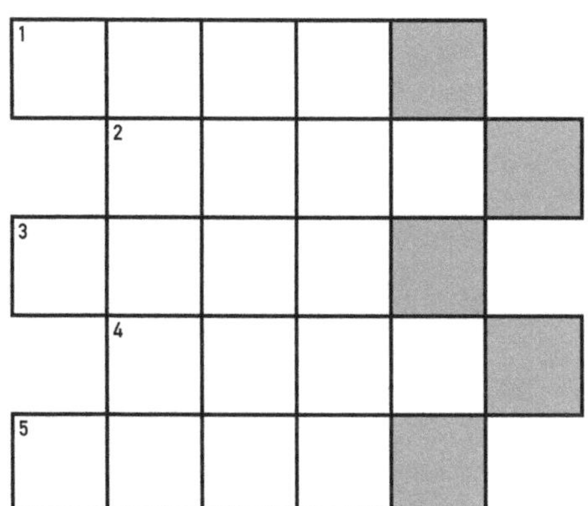

__ __ __ __ __

HELP THE ANTI-VIRUS SOFTWARE BLOCK THE MALWARE

In 2017, organizations all over the world were hit by a WannaCry ransomware attack. Targeting computers operating Microsoft Windows, the malware encrypted data and demanded payment of a ransom to decrypt it. The attack spread quickly affecting 150 countries before a security researcher located a kill switch which severely slowed the attack.

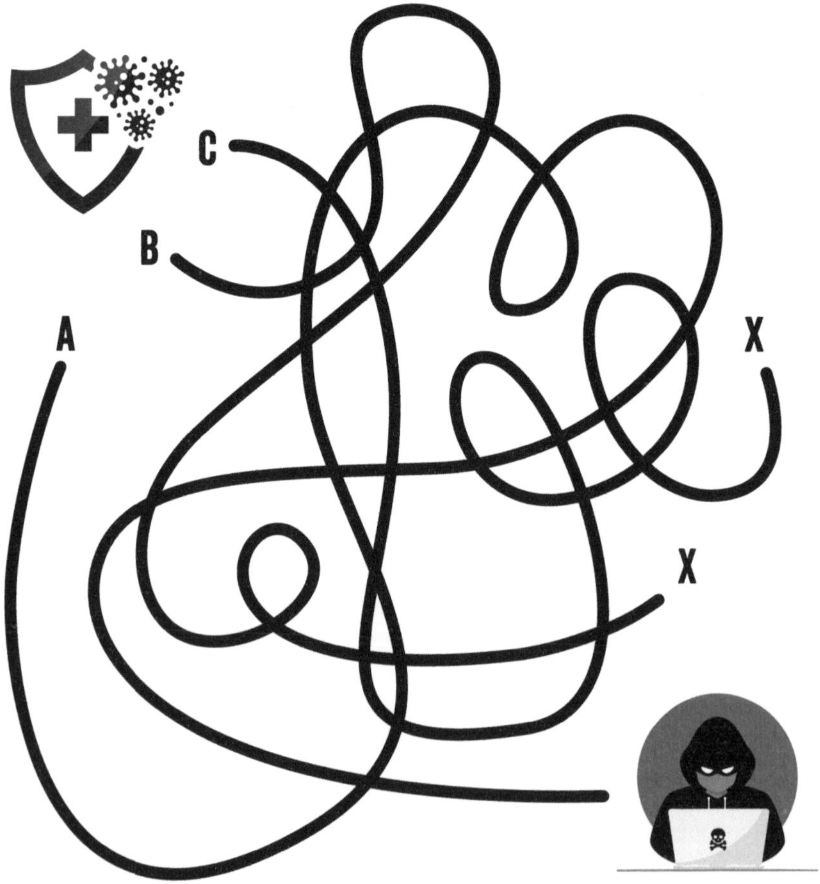

C

B

A

X

X

SUDOKU

Complete the following grid by filling in the empty boxes with the missing numbers. Each number can only appear once in a row, column or box.

		4		8	2	9	6	
8				6				
	9	2	5		7		4	
9	7	8					3	6
	4			9	3			
	3	1					9	8
1	6		4			3	7	9
				3			2	1
	2		1					4

MURDEROUS NUN

From around 1940, the nun Mariam Soulakiotis ran a monastery in Lavreotiki, near Athens, Greece. Marketing the monastery as a tuberculosis treatment centre, Soulakiotis encouraged wealthy women to join the convent and to sign over their savings. Those who joined, including children, were imprisoned, starved and sometimes even killed.

See if you can find the words relating to this shocking case.

```
N I T U P S A R R E H T O M G
X A B B E S S R S Q N P L A F
O F E G M Z X J C Q K L I L O
M W T N B C M M O T I U C N E
F V D U E X T O R T I O N O P
U N H A Z R O M X N S W P U L
Q D O C Z X R Y U U O A T R Z
B Q E R L K T Y P V L B Q I E
Q P G V E S U S P Z A Q T S Q
F P S C M X R D J C T S W H Y
Q R Q K E U E C S J I Q L M X
I Z X R N X H P T B O I D E Z
B B D M T A M H A N N W W N P
I K I T O E R V A L I D D T A
S I S O L U C R E B U T Z G B
```

ABBESS	ISOLATION	LAVREOTIKI
EMBEZZLEMENT	MALNOURISHMENT	TORTURE
EXTORTION	MOTHER RASPUTIN	TUBERCULOSIS

Which American serial killer appeared on the television show *The Dating Game* in 1978?

A. John Wayne Gacy

B. David Berkowitz

C. Rodney Alcala

MOST STOLEN ARTWORK

The most stolen artwork in history is the Ghent Altarpiece by Hubert and Jan van Eyck. It was stolen by Napoleon, repeatedly taken during the First World War and the Second World War, and in 1934 one of its 12 panels was taken, never to be returned.

Can you spot five differences between the images of St Bavo's Cathedral in Ghent, Belgium, where the altarpiece is housed?

BETWEEN THE LINES

A word that describes what drives someone to commit a crime can be inserted in the blank line so that, reading downwards, six three-letter words are formed. What is the hidden word between the lines?

I	T	I	F	I	W
P	P	S	T	Y	T

See how many words of four or more letters you can make, using each letter only once. Each word must use the central letter. Can you find the word meaning arrest that uses all of the letters?

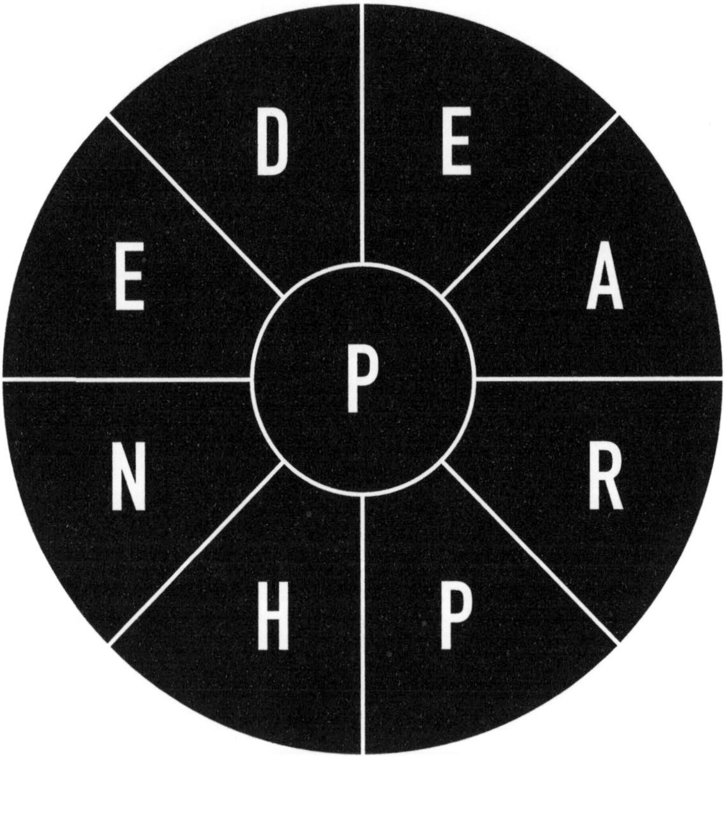

Centre: P

Outer letters: D, E, A, R, P, H, N, E

ANAGRAMS

Rearrange these letters to reveal the weapons assassins use to kill their intended targets.

CRAB MOB

_ _ _   _ _ _ _ _

GARDEEN

_ _ _ _ _ _ _

ELF INSPIRER

_ _ _ _ _ _   _ _ _ _ _ _

Solve the clues correctly and the shaded squares will reveal a word meaning culpability.

1. Juvenile
2. Short Japanese poem
3. Japanese dish
4. Deadly
5. Confess

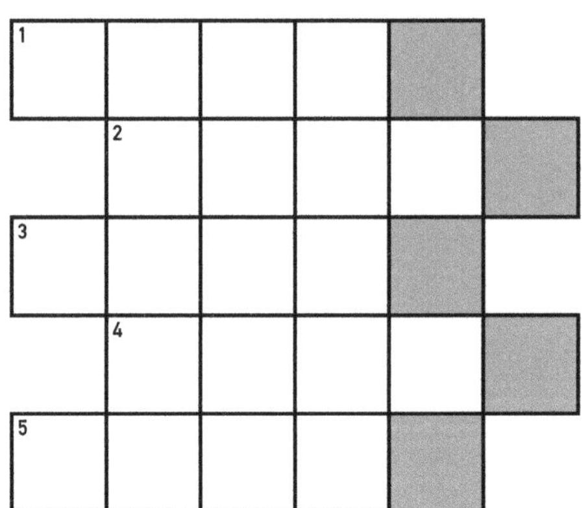

___ ___ ___ ___ ___

COUNTING CONUNDRUM

x = 144

x = 108

− = 9

(+) x = ?

How was the serial killer Richard Ramirez, dubbed the Night Stalker, finally captured in Los Angeles in 1985?

A. By one of his victims who escaped and told the police

B. By a crowd of people who recognized him

C. He turned himself in

HIDDEN WORD

Can you find the nine-letter word, a cause of death, hidden in the grid?

R	A	G
L	T	N
E	S	D

ENDANGERED ELEPHANTS

The trade in wildlife is the fourth biggest illegal trade in the world. Poachers, traffickers and organized crime syndicates source and sell various animal goods, such as elephant ivory, rhino horn and tiger bone, leading to a decline in some of the world's most endangered species.

Can you match up the elephants? The first has been done for you.

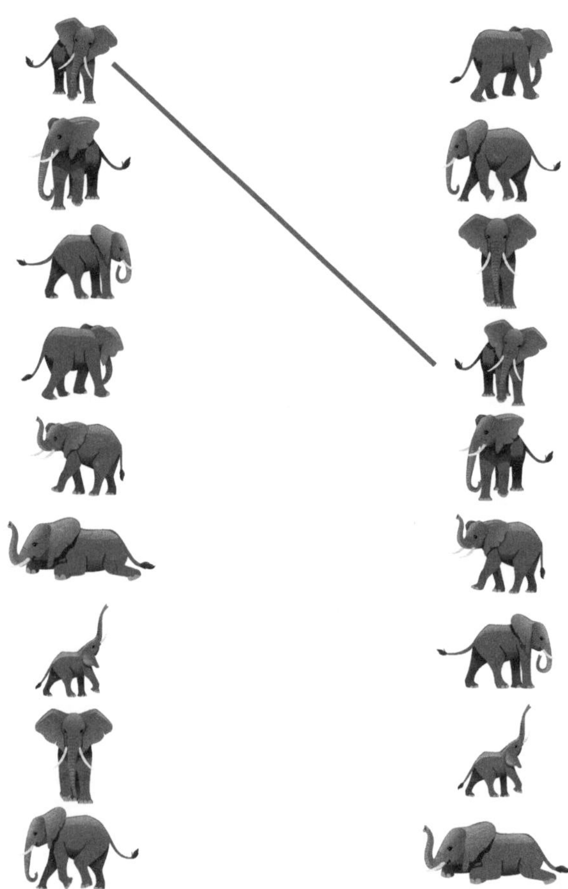

COUNTING CONUNDRUM

+ = 42

+ = 28

− = 10

(x) − = ?

EXTREME FRAUDSTER

Bernie Madoff was behind the biggest financial fraud scheme in US history. He managed to swindle approximately $18 billion out of his investors before his arrest in 2012. Solve the clues to find words linked to his case.

Across

2. Where a vampire keeps his money (7)
5. Fraudulent scheme named after an Italian businessman (5)
6. Putting money in stocks and shares (10)

Down

1. Material lie (11)
3. Putting words in order in court (8)
4. Commodity made by a donkey and an alien (5)

HELP THE POLICE CATCH THE SPEEDBOAT

In 2000, a gang of thieves, heavily armed with machine guns, stormed Sweden's National Museum in Stockholm. Taking the security guards hostage, they stole paintings worth $45 million and then made a James Bond-style escape in a speedboat moored just outside the museum.

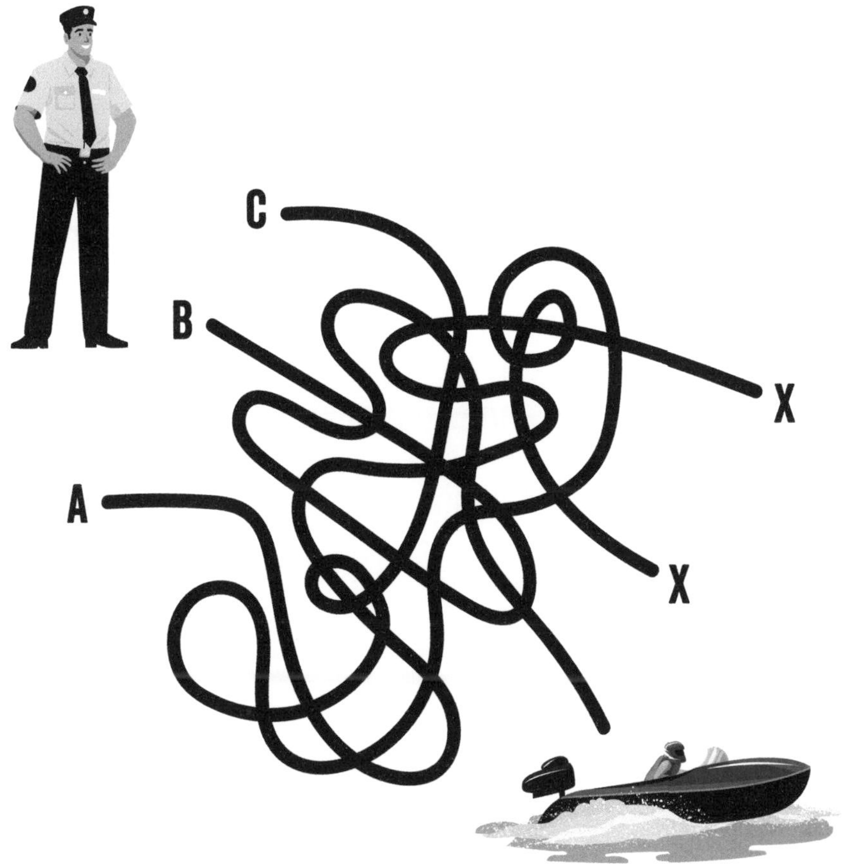

C

B

X

A

X

The death penalty, or capital punishment, has been abolished completely across Europe, except for two countries. Which countries are these?

A. Montenegro and Liechtenstein

B. Estonia and Albania

C. Russia and Belarus

THE PINK PANTHERS

The Pink Panthers are an international network of jewel thieves, responsible for some of the most audacious heists in history. They have been known to steal tens of millions of dollars in diamonds and jewellery, once in a mere 90 seconds.

See if you can find some of the words below relating to the exploits of this notorious gang.

A	R	A	I	T	D	N	A	L	T	R	O	P	G	S
C	Z	E	P	O	R	T	T	N	I	A	S	O	Z	U
P	D	R	I	B	D	C	Z	E	H	H	V	I	G	E
S	M	A	S	H	A	N	D	G	R	A	B	E	S	I
I	Q	J	U	U	G	M	N	Y	C	L	C	E	C	P
G	R	A	F	F	D	I	A	M	O	N	D	S	B	N
V	A	J	Q	F	U	V	E	O	A	K	J	F	N	F
L	Y	T	M	K	B	T	M	N	I	Y	N	S	I	S
E	A	M	U	M	A	I	F	T	E	D	F	L	R	L
V	A	S	N	J	I	A	B	E	P	O	Z	A	Z	Y
I	V	I	V	A	Q	G	J	C	M	A	G	D	I	G
E	L	H	Q	E	Q	A	G	A	P	P	X	L	I	R
V	D	I	J	D	G	P	B	R	C	B	B	T	Z	G
T	E	O	U	T	F	A	W	L	D	O	W	L	C	Y
Y	C	T	X	C	I	J	S	O	A	E	K	M	E	V

DUBAI	LEVIEV	PORTLAND TIARA
GRAFF DIAMONDS	MAYFAIR	SAINT-TROPEZ
LAS VEGAS	MONTE CARLO	SMASH-AND-GRAB

WORD WHEEL

See how many words of four or more letters you can make, using each letter only once. Each word must use the central letter. Can you find the word to describe the people who provide testimonial evidence in court that uses all of the letters?

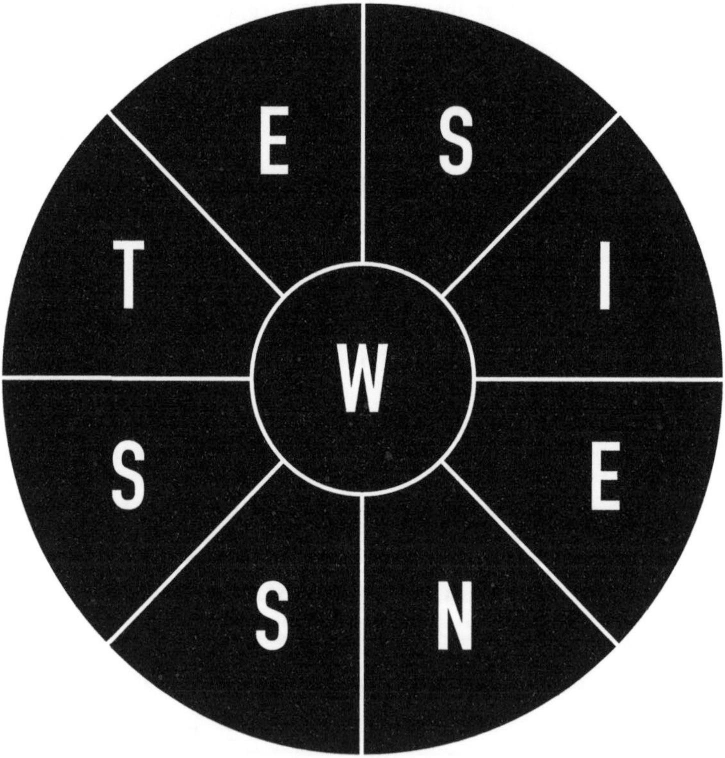

E S I E N S S T

W

ACROSTICS

Solve the clues correctly and the shaded squares will reveal a type of crime.

1. A book or collection of recordings
2. A ballet movement
3. A table used for religious purposes
4. Overflow
5. Opposite of tight
6. Organ that breaks down alcohol

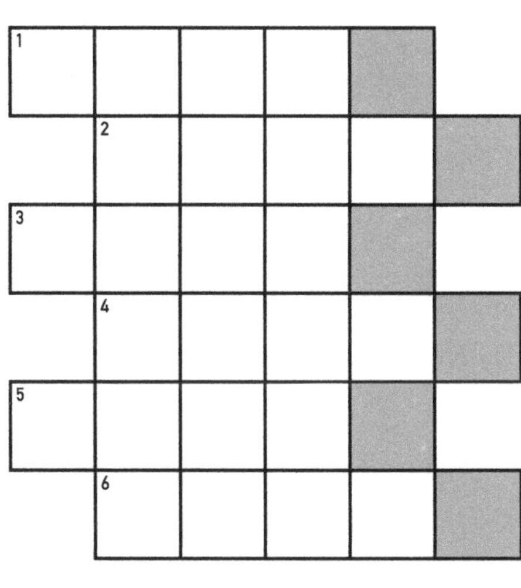

___ ___ ___ ___ ___ ___

Complete the following grid by filling in the empty boxes with the missing numbers. Each number can only appear once in a row, column or box.

								9
2		3		9	5	6	4	7
9	7	6			2		5	8
			4		9	7	2	
				3		9	6	
	9	2	5			8		4
	6							2
8	5							3
3	2		7			5	9	

Which American cult leader was responsible for a series of gruesome murders, including the killing of actress Sharon Tate and several others in 1969?

A. Charles Manson

B. Jeffrey Dahmer

C. John Wayne Gacy

COUNTING CONUNDRUM

+ = 12

+ + = 28

− = 3

(X) − = ?

BETWEEN THE LINES

An unsolved crime can be inserted in the blank line so that, reading downwards, eight three-letter words are formed. What is the hidden phrase between the lines?

A	T	O	O	I	C	U	G
E	P	D	E	Y	T	E	M

SENSATIONAL KIDNAPPING

The kidnapping of the American aviator Charles Lindbergh's son in 1932 made headlines across the world. Despite paying $50,000 in ransom money, the infant's body was discovered two months later. Richard Hauptmann, a German immigrant, was arrested, convicted and executed in 1936.

See if you can find the words relating to the investigation and trial of the Lindbergh kidnapping.

E L E C T R I C C H A I R Y L

Q J S W M J O F T A D V T D I

E G P Q B I E E X U V L G E N

P Q N T K J H T Q I A S T N D

K M G I B S Z H U N F G E R B

X R A A I L W R E R N W N N E

S O D U S V H P A I J S R N R

D T B K Z P H N T E Y Q N A G

W A B A P T S I R O E G L M H

M I L X A O R S U S A R I T J

R V V E M W E B Z E D E D P U

G A D N D Y K G R P K P U U N

X E O N L A D D E R V V R A I

G T A E P Z V L N R X K T H O

E H D U L R M Z V Q A N T F R

AVIATOR
LINDBERGH JUNIOR
DEATH PENALTY
ELECTRIC CHAIR
HANDWRITING
HAUPTMANN
LADDER
NEW JERSEY
RANSOM NOTE

CAR CRIME

Organized crime gangs are increasingly harnessing technology to steal luxury cars. The relay theft method is popular among gangs: they use a portable device that can detect the signal from a car key inside a house, enabling them to unlock a car and drive it away.

Can you spot the five differences between the two images?

Rearrange these letters to reveal three terms relating to court trials.

AXIOM SANCTIONERS

_ _ _ _ _   _ _ _ _ _ _ _ _ _ _ _

MINCED NITT

_ _ _ _ _ _ _ _ _ _

DR EVICT

_ _ _ _ _ _ _

CROSSWORD

VIOLENT CRIME

There are many countries around the world where murder rates are high, and violent and organized crime is a big issue. Solve the clues below to reveal some of the causes and issues behind these high crime statistics.

1
2
3
4
5
6

Across

3. Want or hardship (7)
6. Imbalance (10)

Down

1. Jobless (12)
2. Liquor (7)
4. Criminal groups (5)
5. Firearms (4)

DEADLY AIR ATTACK

In 1985, an Air India flight exploded over the Atlantic Ocean as a result of a bomb planted by terrorists. All 329 people on board were killed, marking this as the world's deadliest act of aviation until the attacks on 11 September 2001 in New York.

Match the aircraft. The first one has been done for you.

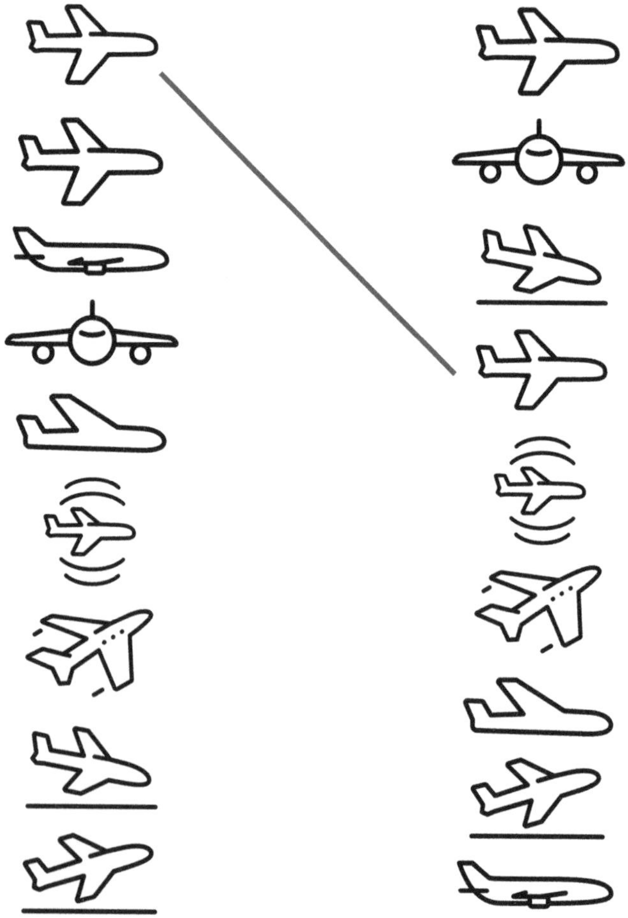

BONNIE AND CLYDE

Bonnie Parker and Clyde Barrow were notorious American outlaws of the 1930s. They were involved in numerous bank robberies and confrontations with the police. Their exploits were covered extensively by the US press and were immortalized in a famous 1967 movie.

Can you spot the five differences between the two images?

EVADE CAPTURE BY THE POLICE

The famous Australian bushranger and outlaw Ned Kelly had numerous clashes with the law during his lifetime. He managed to elude the police for two years, and his most famous act was in 1880 when he and his gang, dressed in plate armour, engaged in a final gun battle with the police. He was eventually hanged, but his legacy lives on as a folk hero of Australia.

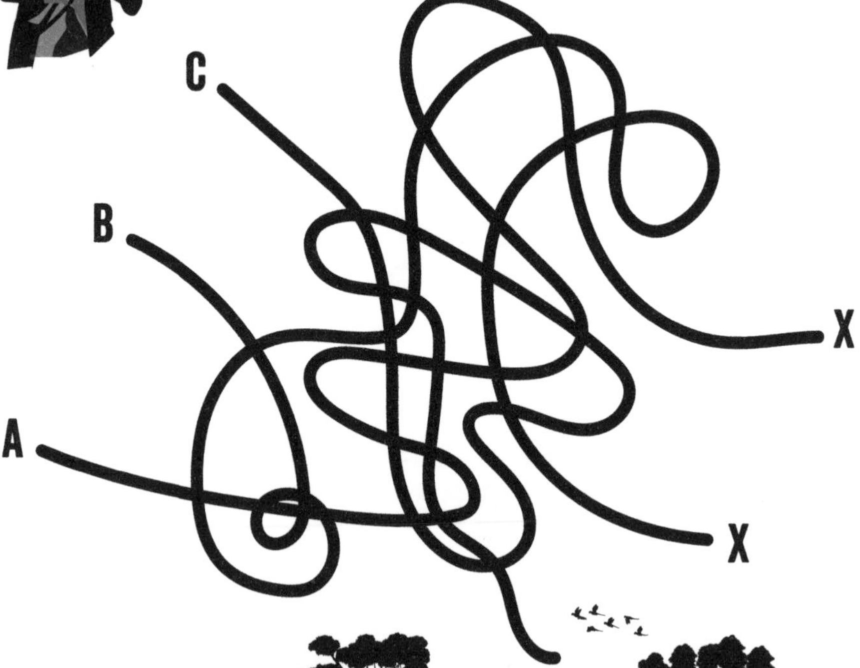

C

B

A

X

X

HIDDEN WORD

Can you find the nine-letter word meaning attacker hidden in the grid?

A	A	I
N	A	L
S	T	S

During the Second World War, the Nazis plundered works of art from countries they had invaded. Which famous museum moved 4,000 of its most precious treasures, including the *Mona Lisa*, to hidden locations?

A. Museo Nacional del Prado, Madrid

B. Austrian Gallery Belvedere, Vienna

C. The Louvre, Paris

UNDERCOVER SURVEILLANCE

When investigating a crime, law enforcers sometimes employ surveillance techniques. By closely observing or following suspects their aim is to catch criminals in the act, providing the evidence they need in court. See if you can stake out the different surveillance techniques below.

G	J	G	P	S	T	R	A	C	K	I	N	G	L	O
V	N	U	C	X	C	Y	E	R	V	M	I	K	H	S
P	N	I	A	T	O	I	N	F	O	R	M	E	R	S
I	W	M	K	F	X	B	R	T	O	Q	G	A	P	T
A	F	K	R	C	U	T	O	T	D	V	D	M	Z	A
P	R	R	Q	E	A	K	M	B	E	Z	F	G	S	K
N	V	E	I	Q	N	R	C	H	L	M	X	X	A	E
T	S	Z	M	Q	M	O	T	T	H	Y	O	W	S	O
Y	I	P	Q	A	Y	U	R	E	O	M	J	I	H	U
R	R	E	V	O	C	R	E	D	N	U	U	R	B	T
E	J	L	S	N	N	V	Q	B	T	O	V	M	C	S
H	A	W	U	V	D	Y	T	M	D	Y	H	Z	A	J
M	J	R	A	P	D	H	O	C	F	G	E	P	J	F
I	R	J	R	H	B	M	A	U	C	J	L	Y	X	C
D	A	T	A	M	I	N	I	N	G	D	W	L	D	N

BIOMETRICS	DRONE	PHONE TRACKING
CCTV CAMERA	GPS TRACKING	STAKEOUTS
DATA MINING	INFORMERS	UNDERCOVER

VINTAGE FRAUD

Rudy Kurniawan was one of the world's biggest wine fraudsters, convicted in 2013 to ten years in a Texan prison. He had been purchasing inexpensive wines, relabelling them with prestigious names and vintages, before selling them on to auction houses, netting millions of dollars in the process.

Match the wine bottles. The first one has been done for you.

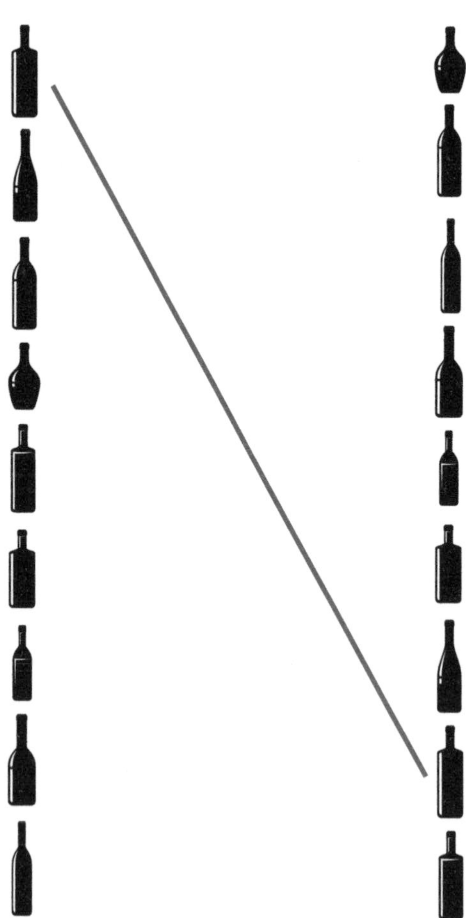

COUNTING CONUNDRUM

\+ = 110

− = 43

x = 169

(+) − = ?

11 SEPTEMBER ATTACKS

On 11 September 2001, terrorists hijacked four commercial airliners and crashed them into the Twin Towers of the World Trade Centre in New York and the Pentagon in Virginia. The attacks, carried out by Islamist militants of Al-Qaeda, killed nearly 3,000 people.

Solve the clues below to reveal further details about the attacks.

Across

3. US invades this country (11)
5. Name of anniversary in US (7, 3)
6. Number of hijackers (8)

Down

1. Twin Tower hit first (5)
2. US state where fourth plane crashed (12)
4. Subsequent name of crash site (6, 4)

In which English town was former Russian military intelligence officer Sergei Skripal and his daughter, Yulia Skripal, poisoned by means of a Novichok nerve agent in 2018?

A. Winchester

B. Salisbury

C. Reading

THE PIED PIPER

Most children know the story of the Pied Piper who led rats from a town into a local river by playing his pipe. Other darker versions of the story depict the piper luring children away as well, which may have stemmed from a real abduction event in 1284 when young people in Hamelin, Germany, apparently went missing.

Can you spot the five differences between the two images below?

HELP SHERGAR THE RACEHORSE ESCAPE THE CRIMINAL GANG

In 1983, a famous racehorse, Shergar, was stolen from his stud in County Kildare in Ireland on a ransom of £2 million. It was thought that the IRA (Provisional Irish Republican Army) had taken the horse, although they have not admitted to it. The horse has never been found.

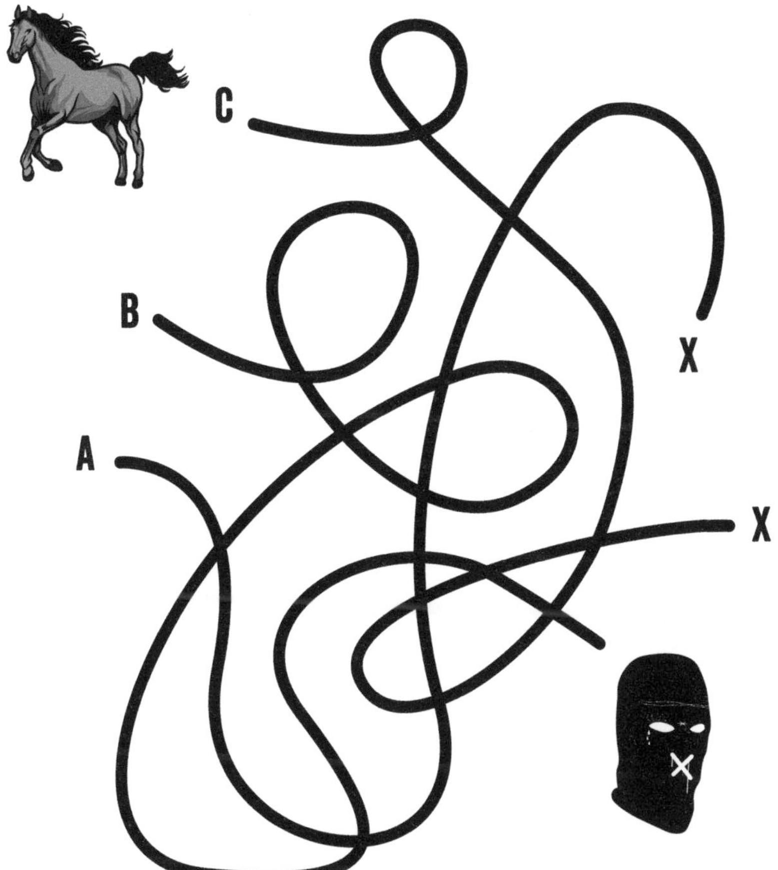

C

B

X

A

X

ANSWERS

1: 1. Duplicates, 2. Getaway car, 3. Preparation, 4. Hairspray, 5. Disable, 6. Plastic gloves

2:

3:

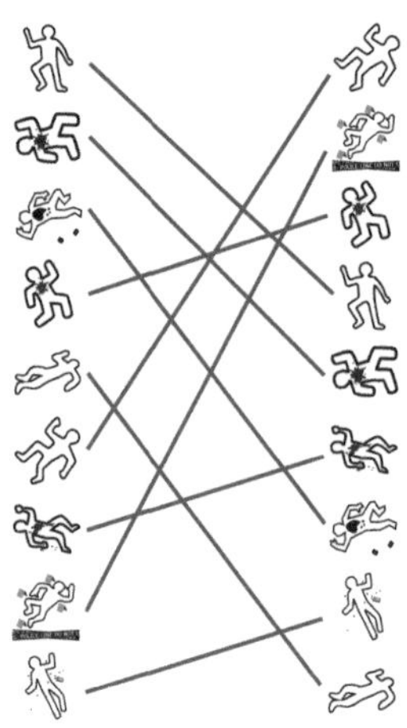

4: A. Finland

5:

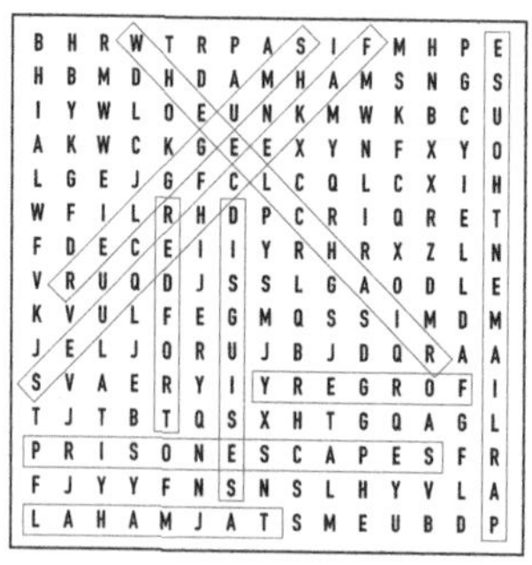

6: = 4, = 12, = 6

(÷) + = 9

7: B

8: Blackmail

9: B. A billionaire female drug boss from Colombia

10: Blindfold

11:

5	8	2	1	6	9	3	7	4
4	3	7	2	8	5	6	1	9
6	1	9	3	4	7	5	2	8
7	5	8	9	3	2	4	6	1
9	2	3	4	1	6	7	8	5
1	4	6	7	5	8	2	9	3
2	7	5	8	9	3	1	4	6
8	6	1	5	7	4	9	3	2
3	9	4	6	2	1	8	5	7

12: Crash, smile, alibi, scams, wrist = HEIST

13: Phishing, smishing, malware

14:

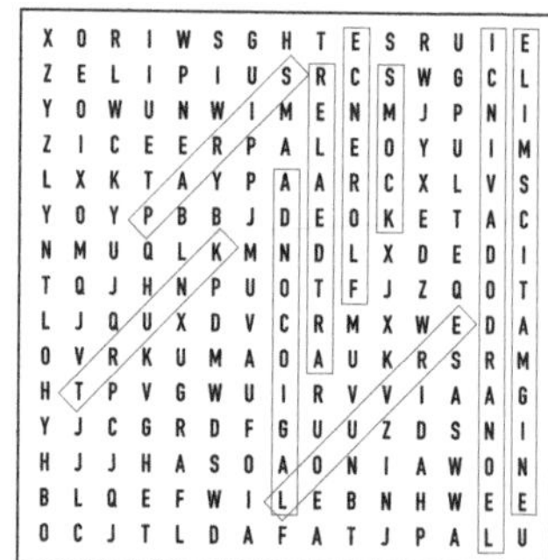

15: Nine-letter word = pathology. Other words = ahoy, aptly, glyph, holy, play, ploy, yoga

16:

17: C. Debbie Harry

18: 1. Soprano, 2. Casino, 3. Scarface, 4. Goodfellas, 5. Donnie Brasco, 6. The Godfather

19: Nine-letter word = extortion. Other words = exon, extort, next, nitrox, oxen, oxer, text, toxin, toxine

20:

21: C

22: Suspect

23: Defrauder

24: Cyanide, arsenic, strychnine

25:

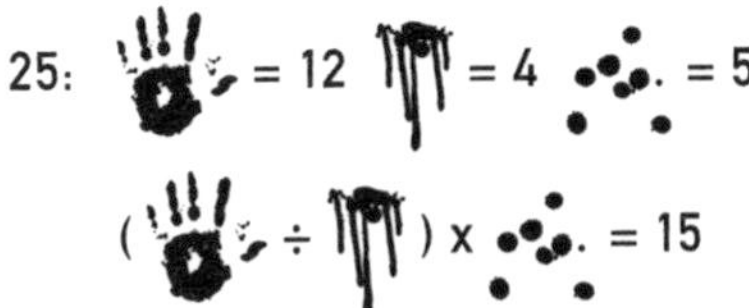

26: 1. Footprint, 2. Blood, 3. Hair, 4. Saliva, 5. Clothing, 6. Fingerprint

27: Bluff, blade, fatal, torso, siren = FELON

28: B

29:

30: Nine-letter word = testimony. Other words = inmost, tome, tone, totem, stone

31: Massacre

32:

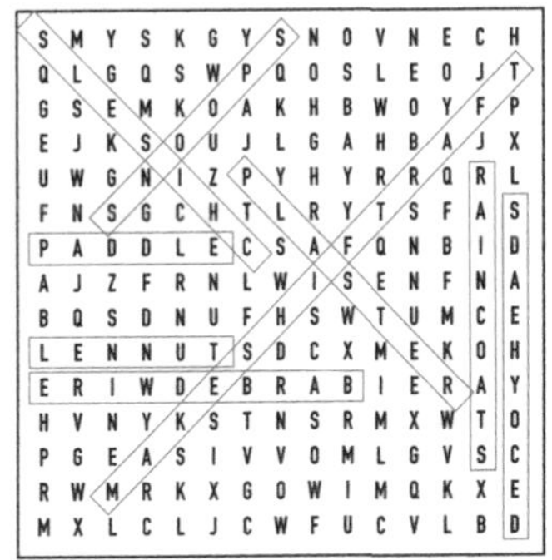

33: Execution

34:

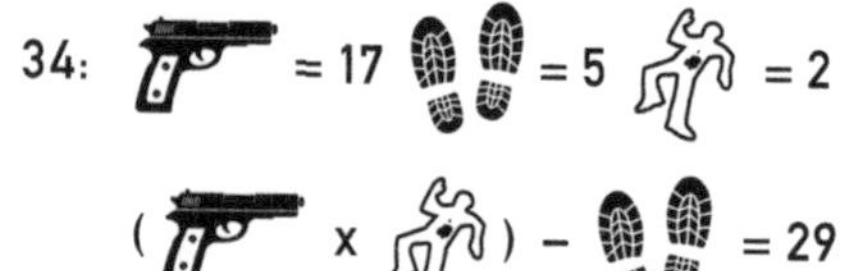

35: Aroma, manor, gloss, cargo, queen = ARSON

36: B. The Zodiac Killer

37:

2	8	6	3	4	1	5	9	7
1	5	4	7	6	9	3	8	2
3	7	9	2	5	8	6	1	4
4	2	1	6	8	3	9	7	5
9	3	8	5	7	4	2	6	1
7	6	5	1	9	2	4	3	8
8	9	2	4	3	7	1	5	6
6	4	7	9	1	5	8	2	3
5	1	3	8	2	6	7	4	9

38: Tiger, pangolin, elephant

39:

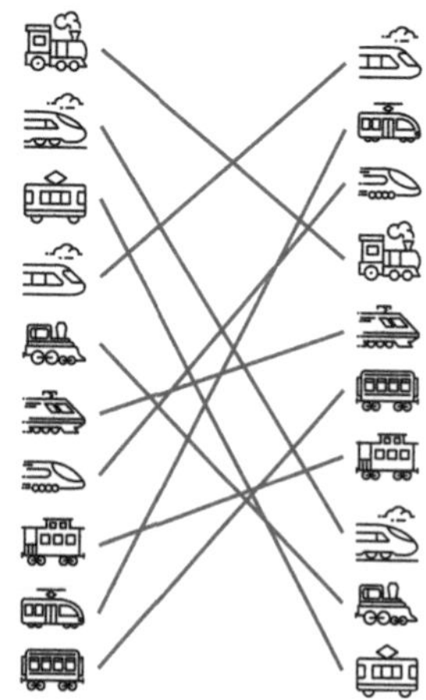

40: Accessory

41: B

42:

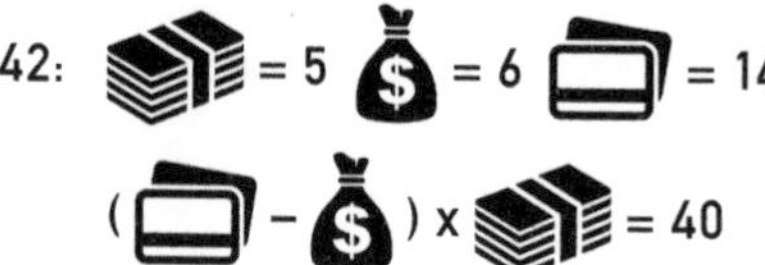

43: Predator

44:

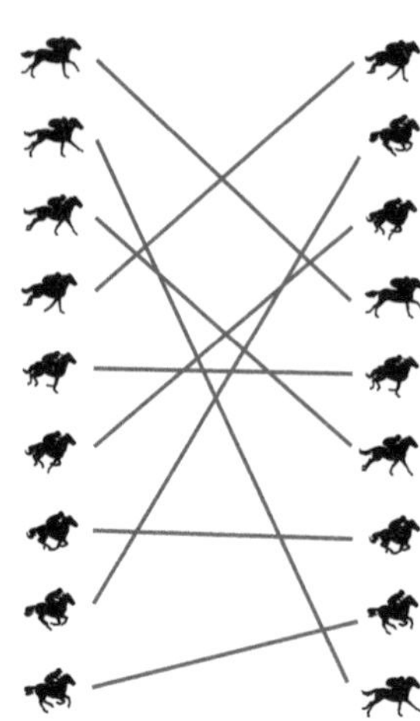

45:

L	T	O	R	X	H	A	K	K	G	O	N	N	L	H
S	E	L	O	P	A	N	A	D	N	E	I	C	A	H
W	V	I	D	F	Q	O	E	V	I	G	M	A	T	A
L	A	R	D	E	T	A	C	A	L	N	W	E	I	S
G	X	K	C	X	C	C	D	T	G	I	Q	I	P	S
Z	E	M	V	U	Q	F	I	B	G	P	M	W	A	A
K	A	J	O	O	Z	G	R	T	U	P	M	W	C	S
C	W	S	I	Q	B	R	N	C	M	A	N	D	R	S
Z	N	I	L	L	E	D	E	M	S	N	B	O	E	I
D	O	W	V	S	F	P	W	S	R	D	J	Q	D	N
D	U	W	Q	J	X	U	L	R	A	I	I	O	R	A
V	M	I	F	O	A	G	G	U	B	K	F	A	U	T
D	S	K	E	B	F	D	O	L	I	X	Y	U	M	I
Z	D	N	U	T	H	D	R	I	O	N	E	G	R	O
R	N	J	E	I	R	E	G	A	N	E	M	R	D	N

46: A. Estonia

47: Rioja, focus, panda, tango, libel = JUDGE

48: Nine-letter word = abduction. Other words = around, conduit, cuboid, daub, doubt, induct, outbid, toucan, unbid

49: Court case

50: 1. Ethnic, 2. Chisel, 3. Six, 4. Italy, 5. Razor, 6. The Mafia

51:

9	8	7	3	4	1	5	6	2
6	2	4	5	8	9	1	3	7
5	3	1	6	2	7	4	9	8
1	7	3	2	9	4	8	5	6
2	5	6	1	3	8	9	7	4
4	9	8	7	5	6	2	1	3
3	1	2	8	7	5	6	4	9
7	6	9	4	1	2	3	8	5
8	4	5	9	6	3	7	2	1

52: Made man, whack, cosa nostra

53: Evidence

54: Nine-letter word = sociopath. Other words = apish, cahoot, cash, chai, chaos, chia, chop, hoist, hoot, pooch, shoot

55: B

56: Scarf, actor, zebra, adieu, duped = FRAUD

57: B. 100

58: 1. Fanny Adams, 2. Red-handed, 3. Pyramid, 4. Shotgun, 5. Highway robbery, 6. Riot

59:

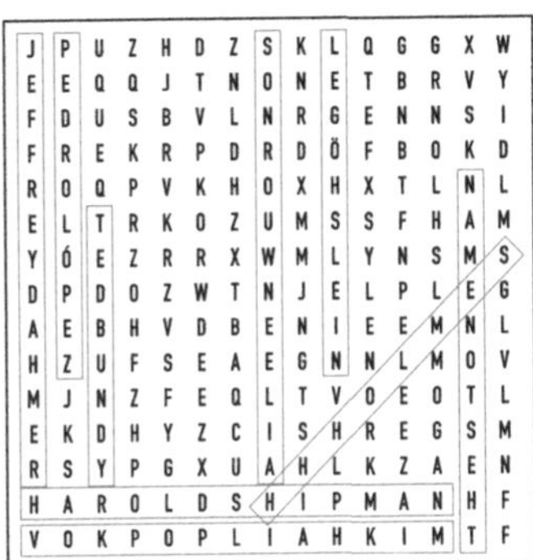

60:

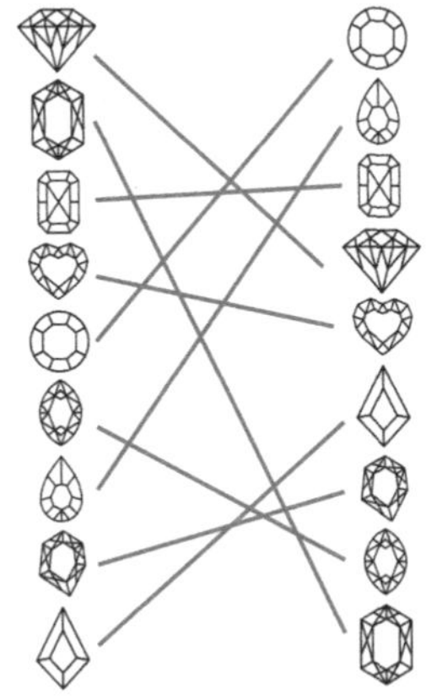

61: CRIME SCENE = 40 ⌖ = 10 🔪 = 3

(CRIME SCENE + ⌖) − 🔪 = 47

62: Lethal injection, electric chair, firing squad

63:

64: C. *The Wolf of Wall Street*

65: B

66: Swindle

67:

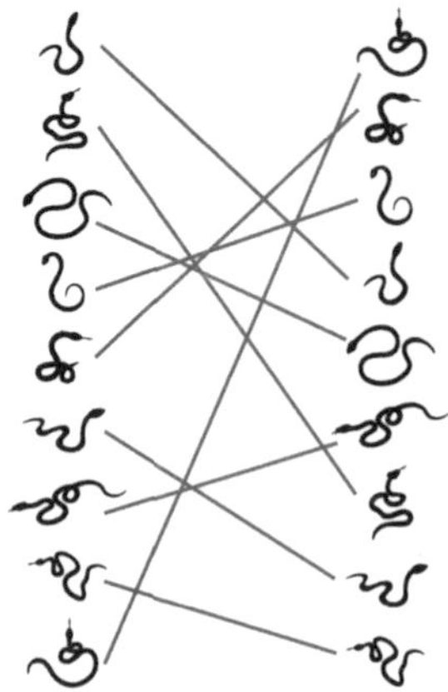

68: B. Gianni Versace

69:

70: 1. Abuse, 2. Addiction, 3. Antisocial, 4. Intelligence, 5. Torture, 6. Arson

71: Kidnapper

72: Forced labour, migrants, smugglers

73:

74:

3	9	7	2	8	1	6	4	5
5	2	8	6	7	4	9	3	1
6	1	4	5	3	9	7	2	8
2	7	9	4	1	8	3	5	6
8	4	5	7	6	3	1	9	2
1	6	3	9	5	2	8	7	4
4	3	2	1	9	6	5	8	7
9	5	1	8	4	7	2	6	3
7	8	6	3	2	5	4	1	9

75: Smoke, agony, avoid, theft, dozen = KNIFE

76:

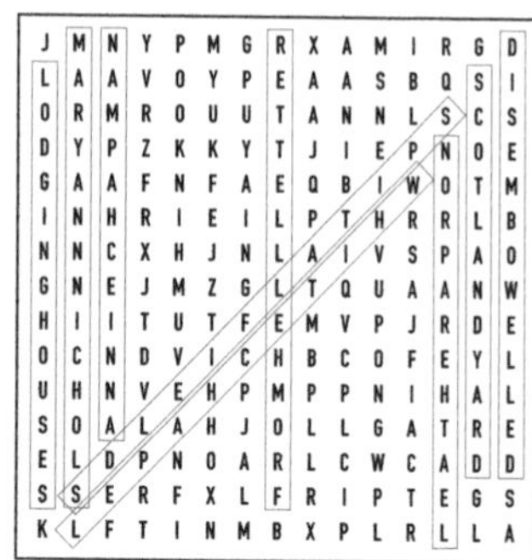

77: Nine-letter word = vandalism. Other words = animal, anvil, dismal, lava, naval, salad, salami, saliva, slam, slim, vandal

78: Autopsy

79: Hush money, black market, filthy lucre

80:

81: C

82: C. Anastasia Romanov

83: = 6 = 10 = 21

(+) – = 17

84:

85: Nine-letter word = forensics. Other words = coif, conifer, confer, fern, fine, fire, force, infer, rife, serif

86: 1. Dragonhead, 2. Yazuka, 3. Macau, 4. Big Circle, 5. Heroin, 6. San Francisco

87: Chess, poppy, opera, honey, poker = SPREE

88: = 17 = 25 = 5

+ + = 47

89: Deception

90: Hustler

91:

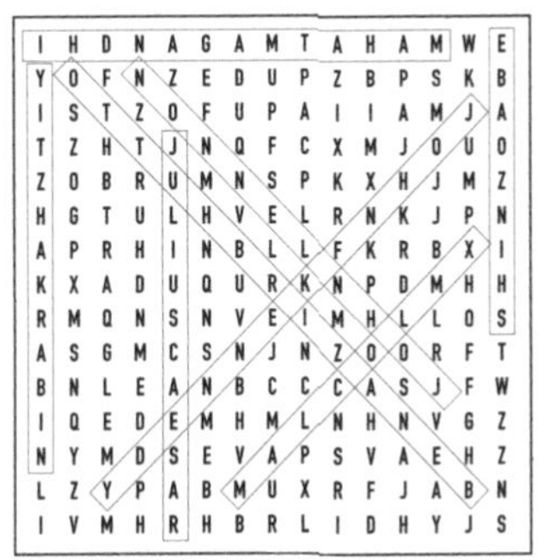

92:

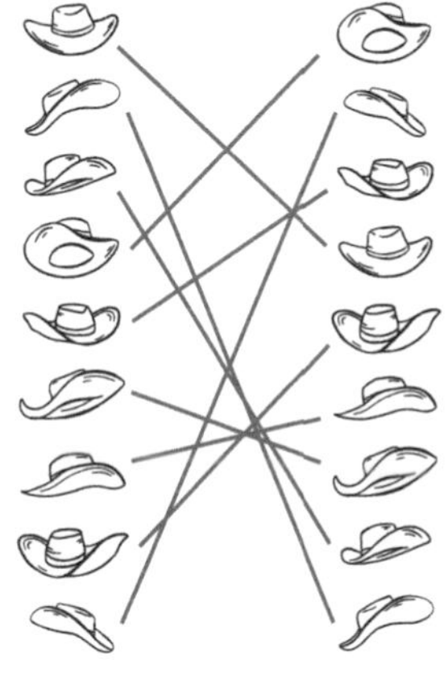

93: 1. Teacher, 2. Lawyer, 3. Pilot, 4. Doctor, 5. Security guard, 6. Police officer

94: B

95:

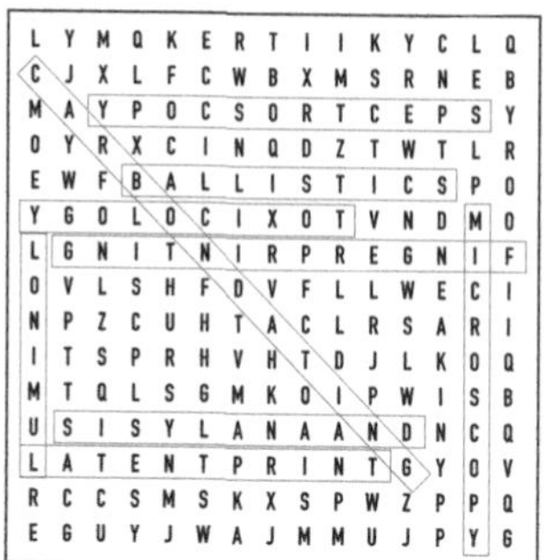

96: C. 35 life sentences plus 1,652 years

97:

98: Nine-letter phrase = cold blood. Other words = blood, bold, clod, cold, cool, dodo, doll

99: Con artist

100: Visionary, hedonistic, mission-oriented

101: 1. Pieces of eight, 2. Galleon, 3. Barbarossa, 4. Blackbeard, 5. Jolly Roger, 6. Francis Drake

102:

103:

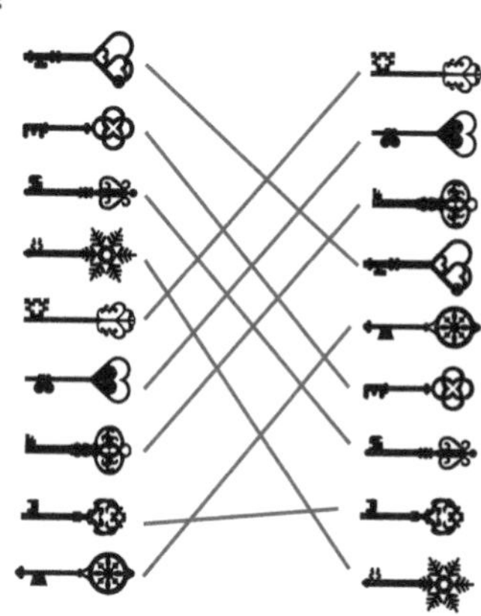

104: Cocoa, growl, emoji, shrub, chili = ALIBI

105: A

106:

7	1	4	3	8	2	9	6	5
8	5	3	9	6	4	7	1	2
6	9	2	5	1	7	8	4	3
9	7	8	2	5	1	4	3	6
2	4	6	8	9	3	1	5	7
5	3	1	7	4	6	2	9	8
1	6	5	4	2	8	3	7	9
4	8	7	6	3	9	5	2	1
3	2	9	1	7	5	6	8	4

107:

N	I	T	U	P	S	A	R	R	E	H	T	O	M	G
X	A	B	B	E	S	S	R	S	Q	N	P	L	A	F
O	F	E	G	M	Z	X	J	C	Q	K	L	I	L	O
M	W	T	N	B	C	M	M	O	T	I	U	C	N	E
F	V	D	U	E	X	T	O	R	T	I	O	N	O	P
U	N	H	A	Z	R	O	M	X	N	S	W	P	U	L
Q	D	O	C	Z	X	R	Y	U	U	O	A	T	R	Z
B	Q	E	R	L	K	T	Y	P	V	L	B	Q	I	E
Q	P	G	V	E	S	U	S	P	Z	A	Q	T	S	Q
F	P	S	C	M	X	R	D	J	C	T	S	W	H	Y
Q	R	Q	K	E	U	E	C	S	J	I	Q	L	M	X
I	Z	X	R	N	X	H	P	T	B	O	I	D	E	Z
B	B	D	M	T	A	M	H	A	N	N	W	W	N	P
I	K	I	T	O	E	R	V	A	L	I	D	D	T	A
S	I	S	O	L	U	C	R	E	B	U	T	Z	G	B

108: C. Rodney Alcala

109:

110: Motive

111: Nine-letter word = apprehend. Other words = dapper, drape, happen, harp, heap, nape, pander, pane, paper, pear, peep, preen, reap

112: Car bomb, grenade, sniper rifle

113: Young, haiku, sushi, fatal, admit = GUILT

114: = 12 = 9 = 18

(+) x = 378

115: B. By a crowd of people who recognized him

116: Strangled

117:

118: = 21, = 7, = 11

(x) – = 56

119: 1. Fabrication, 2. Account, 3. Sentence, 4. Asset, 5. Ponzi, 6. Investment

120: B

121: C. Russia and Belarus

122:

123: Nine-letter word = witnesses. Other words = newest, sewn, sews, sinew, stew, sweet, sweets, swine, Swiss, twin, twine, went, west, wine, wise

124: Album, fondu, altar, flood, loose, liver = MURDER

125:

4	8	5	6	7	3	2	1	9
2	1	3	8	9	5	6	4	7
9	7	6	1	4	2	3	5	8
5	3	8	4	6	9	7	2	1
1	4	7	2	3	8	9	6	5
6	9	2	5	1	7	8	3	4
7	6	9	3	5	4	1	8	2
8	5	1	9	2	6	4	7	3
3	2	4	7	8	1	5	9	6

126: A. Charles Manson

127: = 6 = 11 = 8

(x) - = 58

128: Cold case

129:

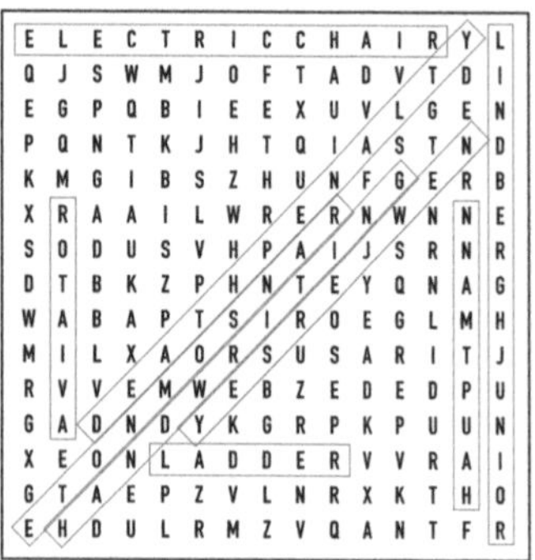

130:

131: Cross examination, indictment, verdict

132: 1. Unemployment, 2. Alcohol, 3. Poverty, 4. Gangs, 5. Guns, 6. Inequality

133:

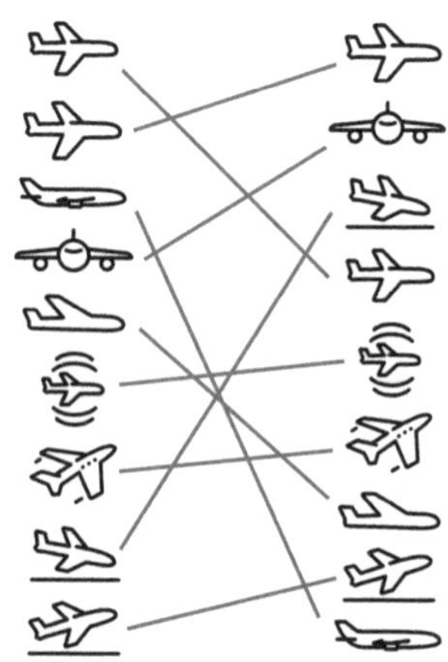

134:

135: C

136: Assailant

137: C. The Louvre, Paris

138:

139:

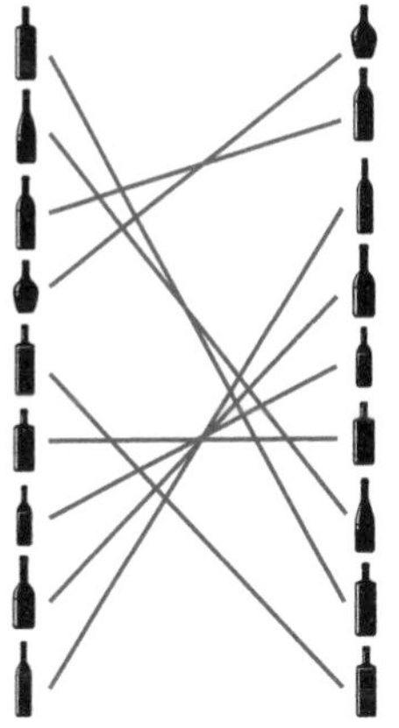

140: = 55 = 12 = 13

(+) – = 56

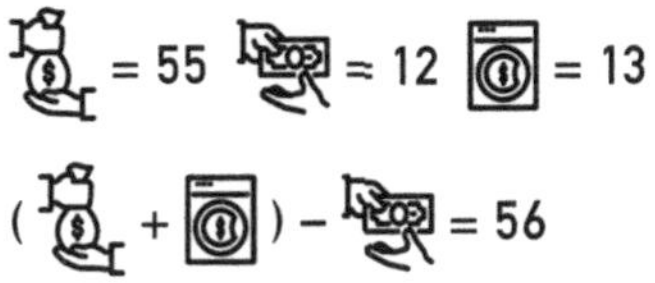

141: 1. North, 2. Pennsylvania,
3. Afghanistan, 4. Ground Zero,
5. Patriot Day, 6. Nineteen

142: B. Salisbury

143:

144: B

THE CONSPIRACY THEORIST'S PUZZLE AND ACTIVITY BOOK

Jamie King

Paperback • ISBN: 978-1-80007-997-7

Test your knowledge of US presidents with fiendish trivia questions

Solve clues to discover how the CIA allegedly control their subjects

Help the reptilian find the right path to its royal throne

Discover some of the most perplexing mysteries that have bewildered humankind for centuries! Dive deep into this book, where the most enduring conspiracy theories are reimagined as puzzles. From crosswords and counting conundrums to spot the differences and sudokus, there's plenty in these pages to keep you questioning the world as you know it.

IMAGE CREDITS

Cover image – cybercriminal © CosmoVector/Shutterstock.com; cover image – handprint © awabsky/Shutterstock.com; cover image – security camera © olahgaris/Shutterstock.com; cover image – knife © WiktoriaMatynia/Shutterstock.com; p.5 – detective board © Tartila/Shutterstock.com; p.6 – chalk outline © EgudinKa/Shutterstock.com; p.6 – chalk outline © ARTYchoke Designs/Shutterstock.com; p.6 – chalk outline © JSlavy/Shutterstock.com; p.6 – chalk outline © Dzm1try/Shutterstock.com; p.6 – chalk outlines © blojfo/Shutterstock.com; p.6 – chalk outline © icon0.com/Shutterstock.com; p.6 – chalk outlines © BNP Design Studio/Shutterstock.com; p.6 – chalk outline © blojfo/Shutterstock.com; p.9 – police officer, car and handcuffs © justone/Shutterstock.com; p.10 – jewellery © kulyk/Shutterstock.com; p.10 – chest © Morgan Ph Shutterstock.com; p.19 – tiaras © vectortatu/Shutterstock.com; p.23 – cybercrime © GreenSkyStudio/Shutterstock.com; p.24 – van © Yuri Schmidtc/Shutterstock.com; p.24 – house © leosapiens/Shutterstock.com; p.28 – blood © PegasuStudio/Shutterstock.com; p.31 – fairies © Shafran/Shutterstock.com; p.31 – girl irina_angelic/Shutterstock.com; p.32 – Alexander the Great © fractalgr/Shutterstock.com; p.37 – gun, footprint and chalk outline © ArnaPhoto/Shutterstock.com; p.42 – trains © blinkblink/Shutterstock.com; p.42 – trains © Picture Window/Shutterstock.com; p.44 – helicopter © Aeronautics Guide/Shutterstock.com; p.44 – skyscraper © Elegant Solution/Shutterstock.com; p.45 – bank notes, money and cards © In-Finity/Shutterstock.com; p.47 – racehorses © VectorArtFactory/Shutterstock.com; p.58 – prisoner © Sabelskaya/Shutterstock.com; p.58 – tunnel © Jozsef Bagota/Shutterstock.com; p.63 – jewels © Tartila/Shutterstock.com; p.64 – tape © siridhata/Shutterstock.com; p.64 – target and knife © newelle/Shutterstock.com; p.66 – festival © GoodStudio/Shutterstock.com; p.68 – maple syrup © RedKoala/Shutterstock.com; p.68 – van © tatianasun/Shutterstock.com; p.70 – snakes © HuHu/Shutterstock.com; p.72 – footprint, fingerprint and magnifying glass © Dervish45/Shutterstock.com; p.76 – kayaker © Alex Darts/Shutterstock.com; p.83 – Eiffel Tower © elena_aldonina/Shutterstock.com; p.84 – police car © Belozersky/Shutterstock.com; p.84 – car © Kotarzewski/Shutterstock.com; p.86 – hacker, skull and bug © 4LUCK/Shutterstock.com; p.87 – bombs © Artur. B/Shutterstock.com; p.91 – camera, scales and prisoner © bsd studio/Shutterstock.com; p.95 – hats © Arlis_art/Shutterstock.com; p.97 – woman © Lana Brow/Shutterstock.com; p.97 – nightclub © Kit8.net/Shutterstock.com; p.100 – bank notes and cards © GoodStudio/Shutterstock.com; p.105 – Victorian lady © ideyweb/Shutterstock.com; p.106 – keys © VectorWeb/Shutterstock.com; p.108 – malware © smx12/Shutterstock.com; p.108 – antivirus © SejalanArt/Shutterstock.com; p.112 – St Bavo's Cathedral © ibrandify gallery/Shutterstock.com; p.117 – figure with bag, handcuffs and prisoner © Cube29/Shutterstock.com; p.120 – elephants © Alfmaler/Shutterstock.com; p.121 – car, gun and siren © davooda/Shutterstock.com; p.123 – police officer © Tartila/Shutterstock.com7; p.123 – speedboat © Vectors Bang/Shutterstock.com; p.130 – robbery, arson and murder © Leremy/Shutterstock.com; p.133 – car © The img/Shutterstock.com; p.136 – planes © matsabe/Shutterstock.com; p.137 – Bonnie and Clyde © Aleutie/Shutterstock.com; p.138 – bushranger © Bradley Buckmaster/Shutterstock.com; p.138 – Australian Outback © shaineast/Shutterstock.com; p.142 – wine bottles © Mallinka1/Shutterstock.com; p.143 – handprints © SpicyTruffel/Shutterstock.com; p.146 – Pied Piper © Luis Line/Shutterstock.com; p.147 – racehorse © Bimantra/Shutterstock.com; p.147 – balaclava © SergeyBitos/Shutterstock.com

Have you enjoyed this book?

If so, find us on Facebook at **SUMMERSDALE PUBLISHERS**, on Twitter/X at **@SUMMERSDALE** and on Instagram and TikTok at **@SUMMERSDALEBOOKS** and get in touch.

We'd love to hear from you!

WWW.SUMMERSDALE.COM